101

Ways to Improve Your Personal Training Business

Jeremy Koerber and Kathy Bretsch

HEALTHY LEARNING™

ISBN: 978-1-60679-103-5
Library of Congress Control Number: 2010924344
Cover design: Brenden Murphy
Book layout: Studio J Art & Design
Front cover photos: (top) Medioimages/Photodisc; (bottom) Comstock
Back cover photo (authors): Steve Frazier

Healthy Learning
P.O. Box 1828
Monterey, CA 93942
www.healthylearning.com

Dedication

This book is dedicated to our families, who continue to support us through our business adventures, and the numerous mentors who have shown us the way to better serve our customers throughout the years. Thank you.

Foreword

The world does not need another mediocre "how-to" fitness book, but it certainly deserves a great one. This book fills a need that so oftentimes goes overlooked in the fitness industry in the realm of personal training. As I discuss at length in my book *Cream Rises: Excellence in Private and Group Education*, the two big fields of personal training (and group fitness, for that matter) are the "what" we train, and the "how" we train it. Today, so many websites, magazine articles, and books direct themselves to the "what." These items discuss how to get certified, what to train with clients, and, above all, muscles and movements to create magic with the body. We need more texts like *101 Ways to Improve Your Personal Training Business* that dedicate themselves to *how* we create a business to train people. Truly, this business is one in which we help make people champions of living as certified lifestyle motivational empowerment experts.

Jeremy and Kathy's book fills a void in the fitness industry. The authors are ready to help each personal trainer with new—yet practical—ideas to boost business. One chapter outlines real-life lessons on making a fitness business plan for your personal-training business, something no certification company discusses when preparing individuals when obtaining initial certifications. Another chapter details the specifics of marketing personal training to gain new clients, generate productivity, and ultimately, increase revenue by having a successful bottom line.

Unlike other texts that are out there that I have been asked to endorse, this book offers successful tips because, quite simply, the author is the definition of successful. If you were to open the fitness dictionary for 2009 and look up the words "successful personal trainer living what he preaches," the definition would be: Jeremy Koerber. Jeremy has been exuding his strong entrepreneurial skills in a plethora of markets in the greater St. Louis area for many years, with the litmus-testing proofs of success that only personal trainers understand: accolades from his superiors, waiting lists of clients wanting to book him for personal training, teaching engagements as a trainer of trainers, and successful, trailblazing ideas implemented as his various places of employment like the BJC WellAware Center, a medically-based fitness facility associated with BJC HealthCare, one of the largest nonprofit health-care organizations in the United States. Kathy Bretsch has more than 12 years of experience in health-care marketing and communications and is one of the most-sought-after freelance writers in the St. Louis region with clients from one of St. Louis's largest employers and a Fortune 500 company.

Among the most ubiquitous of questions I receive daily from hundreds of e-mails is "I'm certified, but now what do I do?" My answer can now be a confident "Read Jeremy and Kathy's book."

Lawrence Biscontini, MA
International Fitness Trainer,
Lecturer, Spa Consultant,
and Entrepreneur

Contents

Dedication 3
Foreword 4
Introduction 9

Chapter 1: The Marketing Plan: What You Need to Know 11
   1.   What Would You Like Your Business to Become?
   2.   What Are You Selling?
   3.   You've Got to Have a Plan
   4.   What Do You Do Well?
   5.   Identifying Opportunities
   6.   Timing Is Everything
   7.   Creating a Competitive Advantage
   8.   SWOT Your Competition
   9.   What Is Your Mission in Life?
   10.   What Do You Have to Sell?
   11.   Assessing Your Share
   12.   What Are Your Four Ps?—The Marketing Mix
   13.   Who Is Your Market?
   14.   The Economic Environment
   15.   The Competitive Environment
   16.   Capitalizing on Changes in Technology
   17.   Society's Impact on Personal Training
   18.   Legal and Regulatory Considerations
   19.   The Marketing Plan—Going From Where You Are to Where You Want to Be

Chapter 2: Product—It's More Than What You're Selling .43
   20.   Defining Your Product
   21.   Creating Your Product Mix
   22.   Product Positioning
   23.   Finding Your Niche
   24.   Evolving Your Product Line
   25.   Product Deletion
   26.   Building Your Brand
   27.   Who Are You?

28. How Valuable Is Your Brand?
29. Co-Branding for Success
30. Bob's Personal Training—Selecting a Brand Name
31. Protecting Your Investment
32. Making the Intangible Tangible
33. Product Life Cycle

Chapter 3: Price—Deciding How Much to Charge 59
34. Pricing Decisions
35. Pricing Objectives
36. Setting Prices
37. Price Discounting
38. Competitor Pricing
39. Positioning From a Pricing Standpoint
40. Determining Value in Your Pricing

Chapter 4: Promotion—Getting the Word Out 67
41. Hey, Look at Me!—Promotion Decisions
42. Advertising
43. Advertising Legalities
44. Sales Promotion
45. The Role of Newsletters
46. Cross-Promotion
47. Putting Public Relations to Work for You
48. Identifying New Prospects
49. Personal Selling
50. Closing the Sale
51. The World of Online Marketing
52. Launching a Website to Market Your Business
53. Making Your Website Valuable
54. Display Ads
55. Pay Per Click
56. Search Engine Optimization
57. E-mail Marketing
58. To Blog or Not to Blog: That Is the Question
59. Viral Marketing
60. Is YouTube for You?
61. Posting on Message Boards
62. Becoming the Local Fitness Expert—How to Get Noticed
63. E-Books
64. Social Media
65. How to Find Yourself on Yahoo!

Chapter 5: Placement—How and Where Your Product Will Be Distributed 101
   66.   Expand Your Business by Marketing to Businesses
   67.   Subcontracting to Generate New Business
   68.   Penetrating the Business Market
   69.   Getting Past the Gatekeeper
   70.   Fitting the Product to the Client
   71.   For a Good Cause
   72.   Partnering Up

Chapter 6: It's All About the Relationships 113
   73.   Forging Relationships That Matter
   74.   Community Relations
   75.   Networking
   76.   Managing Clients
   77.   Finding a Mentor Who Matters

Chapter 7: General Tips 121
   78.   Getting Specific
   79.   Persuading the Consumer
   80.   Identifying Wellness Opportunities for Businesses
   81.   Opportunity Knocks
   82.   Building Loyalty Through Ethics
   83.   Creating Quality
   84.   Service Quality
   85.   Understanding Your Customers' Perception of Value
   86.   Duplicate Yourself
   87.   Supplements and Nutritional Products
   88.   Building Your Business on the CICE Principles
   89.   How to Run a Marketing Campaign
   90.   How's Your Posture?
   91.   Learning to Adapt
   92.   A Little Attitude Goes a Long Way
   93.   Think About the Big Picture
   94.   Generating Ideas
   95.   Taking an Idea for a Test Drive
   96.   Educate Yourself About the World of Business
   97.   Making the Most of Your Time
   98.   When to Call in the Experts
   99.   Sometimes It Is Who You Know
  100. Are You Covered?
  101. Pulling It All Together

Recommended Websites and Blogs 150
References and Recommended Reading 151
About the Authors 152

Introduction

You worked hard and earned the degree. You completed your certifications, obtained professional liability insurance and have gotten the word out about your fitness services. Congratulations! You are a personal trainer in business for yourself. Those feelings of satisfaction only multiply when you land that first client. Now all you have to do is develop an exercise prescription and provide the necessary motivation and support to help the client succeed, right?

Well, you are partly right. To make significant strides in your business, you need a plan—a plan to keep your new client long enough to see them meet their objectives, attract more customers along the way to make a profit, pay your expenses, and keep your business afloat in a highly competitive market.

Today's fitness consumers are bombarded with information—information about fitness centers, personal trainers, supplements, diets plans, and equipment. The Internet is a virtual bottomless well of information for health and wellness, and this represents your competition. Trainers are a dime a dozen. Many do-it-yourself fitness books are available, and you can even have a trainer develop exercise programs on the Internet. At this point, you need to ask yourself a few questions:
- What is my product?
- Who are my clients?
- Who are my competitors?
- Do I have a business plan?
- How am I going to grow my business?

Oftentimes, young professionals are very well-educated in exercise science and program design but lack the skills to build a solid business. It isn't that they are bad trainers; in fact, some of the best trainers in fitness have gone belly-up because they did not understand how to grow their business and create a solid brand identity that sets them apart from their competitors.

101 Ways to Improve Your Personal Training Business is a step-by-step manual to help you build a profitable personal-training business from the ground up. The book is designed to give you easy-to-follow marketing tools that will help you define your product, locate your target market, develop a business plan, and ultimately grow your business.

There has never been a better time to be in the fitness industry. Approximately 78.2 million baby boomers (estimated by the U.S. Census Bureau as of 2005) on the verge of retirement have the desire to fight the aging process and the income to pay for these services. More fitness centers are available today than ever before. Companies are beginning to catch on that a healthier employee is a happier, more productive employee. And everyone from senior citizens to soccer moms are looking for ways to ward off disease, bolster performance, and improve their looks through exercise and proper nutrition. The customers are out there. How do you plan to drive them to your door? Our mission is to give you the tools necessary to locate, attract, and meet the needs of prospective customers who will be looking to you for the answers. So sit back, grab a pen and paper, and begin working the chapters one at a time. Very soon, you will understand and have the skills to grow your training business.

1

The Marketing Plan:
What You Need to Know

Jupiterimages

#1: What Would You Like Your Business to Become?

What are your business goals? This question may sound like a silly statement, but far too often entrepreneurs from all walks of life enter into business ventures with no clearly stated objectives and goals for what they want to achieve and how they plan to achieve them. As a fitness professional, you ask each of your clients to list their health and fitness objectives because you know the importance of setting measurable goals to attain success. It shouldn't be any different when it comes to your personal training business.

At the very least, your primary objective should be to operate a business that is profitable because without profit, there is a good chance you will not be in business very long. Customer satisfaction also needs to rank high on your list of objectives because without satisfying exchanges between the trainer and the client, the likelihood of a longstanding relationship is bleak.

Think back to past job interviews in which you've been asked about goals—immediate, mid-range, and long-term. Next, translate that exercise for your business. A common acronym used in business when developing objectives is to make them SMART: Specific, Measurable, Attainable, Realistic, and Timely.

Specific goals have a much greater chance of being accomplished. Stating measurable objectives—such as total revenue generated per quarter or total sessions performed per month—makes it much easier to stay on track, reach your targets, and continuously improve. Attainable goals are those that are realistic given your resources. A goal to increase your client list from 25 to 50 in one month may not be realistic; that's a 100-percent increase. A realistic goal is one that you have to be willing and able to pursue. Timely goals, that is, setting them to be achieved within a certain time frame, helps to create a sense of urgency.

Jill Harbert had a very simple objective when she started Fitness Forte, a personal-training company in St. Louis, Missouri: to be her own boss. "I was very young when I started my business. I knew that if a business could make it in three to five years, then it had great chances at success. But those three to five years could be pretty up and down. Personal training is a business based on customer service, and I have long since striven to achieve excellent customer service. I want my clients to feel well taken care of."

Jill's goal was simple. She needed to generate enough revenue to keep her business alive, and she needed loyal, satisfied clients to make this happen. Four years later, Fitness Forte is strong and growing.

If you're already in business, take some time to evaluate where you are and where you want to go. If you're just getting started, before launching into developing client relationships, you need to know where you envision taking your business. Either way, whether it's a part-time venture to generate extra cash on the side or an international fitness empire that you're after, it all starts with a plan.

Exercise

Develop a list of SMART goals you wish to achieve in one, three, and five years.

One Year:
1.
2.
3.

Three Years:
1.
2.
3.

Five Years:
1.
2.
3.

#2: What Are You Selling?

According to the American Marketing Association, a product is a good, service, or idea that is exchanged with a customer to complete a business transaction. In the business owner's terms, it's what you do for your customers, whether it's a sale of a tangible item or a service. A personal-training session is a service you are providing. Supplements—such as fish-oil capsules or whey protein powder—are goods. Sharing your philosophies about weight loss with a client is about selling an idea. So the question is: what is your product (or products)?

Ask a personal trainer that question and, no doubt, the answer would be conducting personal-training sessions, but the way personal training has evolved since its inception years ago, there are more ways to create revenue than by standing in front of a client. Unless you have the ability to charge higher fees for your services or plan to live 24/7 in the gym, you will have a tough time sustaining your business.

Instead, take inventory of the many ways you can take what you know and develop those skills into a line of products and services that can generate additional cash flow. For example, if personal training is your primary product, a number of different product categories such as the following can be added to your mix of products and services.

- *One-on-one training*: This is the most traditional concept where the trainer meets with one client at a time.
- *Small group training*: Working with small groups of two to four clients with similar interests and fitness level enables clients to pay a lower price per session, but the trainer makes double to triple the revenues. For example, if you charge $60 per session you will have to train two hours to generate $120. If you train four clients at $30 per session you will make $120 in one hour.
- *In-home training*: Taking your services into a client's home can, in many cases, make the client more comfortable with training. Typically, trainers can charge higher prices to account for travel time.
- *Online personal training and coaching*: Millions of dollars are spent each year on exercise books, diet plans, and exercise DVDs. Consumers who are willing to spend money for books and DVDs may also be open to online coaching and training. This service also can be provided anywhere at any time. You can train clients in your pajamas!
- *Nutritional products*: Some trainers are reluctant to market nutritional products to their clients, but they are missing a golden opportunity to generate additional revenue. Of course, you need to determine what types of products to market and why you intend to offer them to your customers. It also needs to be a product that you use, are familiar with, and has been proven to provide benefit without risk to your customers. The hot products today are omega-3 fatty acid capsules and whey

protein. If you don't have the resources to store inventory, many companies feature distributor programs and offer commissions for recommending products to your customers.

- *Boot camps*: Again, much like the concept of small-group personal training, you can generate revenue even when charging a lower price per client because of the volume of customers. For example, enrolling 20 participants in an early-morning boot camp at $10 per person generates more revenue than three one-on-one sessions at $60 an hour.
- *E-books*: If you're a closet John Grisham, take your experiences and skills, and write a book that can be sold directly through a website—preferably your own.

Remember to think outside the box, and don't limit yourself. You have the ability to differentiate yourself from other trainers by offering a mix of goods, services, and ideas that can generate additional revenue for your business. Start with a list of ideas, and see where it can take you.

Exercise

Brainstorm a list of 10 ways you can develop new products to market to your customer base.

1.
2.
3.
4.
5.
6.
7.
8.
9.
10.

#3: You've Got to Have a Plan

Now that you have defined what products you will be offering to your target market, you need to develop a strategic marketing plan. According to the American Marketing Association, strategic planning is the process that helps a business make decisions for how it will plan to compete in the marketplace. Some components of the strategic planning process can include:

- Developing a mission for your business
- Setting goals
- Determining how resources will be used in your business
- Developing marketing objectives
- Developing a market strategy
- Writing a business plan

Now is the time to think about the big picture. It may seem daunting, but in a realistic tone, take inventory of what resources you have available, how you intend to use those resources to grow your business, and what your objectives are for the fiscal year. Then, start asking yourself some specific questions to help outline your direction.

- What is your business?
- Who are your customers?
- What do you do really well?
- What opportunities are in the current marketplace?
- Using answers from these four questions, what are your business objectives for this fiscal year?
- What are some possible strategies you can use to meet these objectives?

This is a planning process, and it is meant to get you thinking about more than how many sets and reps your 3 p.m. client will perform in their next session. Too often, many personal-training businesses fail because the owners lack the vision to design a business model that will improve their odds of surviving in a highly competitive industry. You may have a full client load full of individuals making New Year's resolutions in January, but will those same clients be with you in July?

The next few sections will break down the strategic planning process step by step. Answer these questions, and paint a portrait of your training business. Now is the time to lay the foundation for a strong business model that will increase your chances of success.

#4: What Do You Do Well?

Personal trainers have the tendency to try to be all things to all people. Whether it's helping a client lose weight or teaching someone to work on core strength to improve their golf game, trainers become jacks-of-all-trades. Unfortunately, businesses that try to be all things to all people rarely succeed. This does not mean you have to limit who you target as clients, but you do need to understand your strengths and how to capitalize on them. You need to understand your core competencies.

Core competencies are things a business does very well, the things you do so well that they give you an advantage over the competition. Chances are you have experienced this to some degree in your training business but did not realize it. Perhaps you have a reputation in your gym for being the resident expert on weight loss, sports-specific training, or older clientele. Your natural ability to work with specific type(s) of clients attracts them to you. For example, you could be known for understanding the particular health benefits of elderly clients. They seek your expertise and skill in developing safe, effective programming that considers potential health problems of disease or aging. Your ability to relate with this group is a core competency.

This is not saying you cannot train other types of clients. Instead, capitalize on your strengths, and make that group or demographic the focus of your business. Building a strong business is not about reinventing the wheel or becoming a master at all areas in health and wellness, nor do you have to be the first trainer to come up with a new, innovative concept to meet the needs of a market.

A wise person knows what he is good at and uses that to improve himself. When you train clients, you develop programs based upon what the client does well and build from there. Use these same techniques to grow your business, and you will be ahead of the trainer who is still searching for his place in the fitness industry.

Exercise

Make a list of five core competencies in your training business.

1.
2.
3.
4.
5.

#5: Identifying Opportunities

January is the month that every fitness center, trainer, and recreation facility in the country offers special promotions. Why? To take advantage of the millions of Americans making New Year's resolutions and searching for the formula to help them lose weight, improve their health, and look better. It's the hottest time in the fitness industry, and facility managers and trainers would be fools not to take advantage of these opportunities. Yet while the New Year represents the easiest time period to bring in new clients, it's just one of the many opportunities that arise throughout the year. Successful businesses cannot be built once a year.

So how do you identify those opportunities and reach your target market with offers for your services or products? By keeping your eyes and ears open. In many cases, the timing of events around you, coupled with action on your part, can create new opportunities for increased business. For example, consider extending the New Year's rush to include college students wanting to get ready for spring break. The high cost of one-on-one training during an economic downturn could be a perfect situation to offer either group personal training or online training.

Consider starting a boot camp for stay-at-home moms who are looking for a way to get out of the house, socialize, and shed some weight before the family vacation. Or develop a low-impact flexibility class to help the older members of your church you've heard complaining about arthritis improve their range of motion and function.

Keep on top of what is going on in the world. Medical studies making headlines will create opportunities. New studies on exercise, disease prevention, or nutrition can lead to ideas for building your business. Industry journals such as *Club Industry* and organizations such as the American College of Sports Medicine are also excellent sources of industry-specific news.

Organizations such as the Missouri Hospital Association distribute yearly promotional schedules at no cost that promote or recognize health-related professions, accomplishments, and special observances such as Healthy Weight Week and Cholesterol Education Month. Use these publications to help identify market opportunities. Stay in tune with what's going on in your community and in the world of health and fitness. Opportunities abound!

Goodshoot

#6: Timing Is Everything

Timing is everything. It's a phrase you've probably heard often. A great deal of truth can be found in that statement, especially when it comes to your business. Combining your best attributes with opportunities in the marketplace in a timely manner is paramount to your success. The previous section explored the need to seek opportunities around every corner. However, it's equally important to be ready to pounce when a strategic window presents itself in the marketplace: timing.

The January rush for a personal trainer can be compared to tax season for an accountant. It is the most important time of year where a trainer can make a huge impact in the market they serve. Unfortunately, fitness professionals who do not prepare adequately will fail to identify opportunities before their competition. For example, advertising services in a local newspaper in January may be too late to take advantage of those wanting to shed holiday pounds starting January 2. The ad should have begun running in December.

Spring and early summer are the wedding seasons. Consider marketing to wedding planners or brides-to-be to take advantage of the growing number of brides who want to be in tip-top shape for their wedding day. But don't wait until April; many May and June brides will have already begun training for their big day in February, if not before.

To grow your business, you have to know what you do well, what opportunities are available in your marketplace, and how to connect the two before the window of opportunity is closed. Be proactive, and plan ahead. Some trainers plan as much as a year out to ensure they have every season covered to maximize their potential revenues and run a healthy training business. Do not be afraid to think outside the box, because the next great idea might fall into just the right window of opportunity.

Exercise

Identify and match up five of your core competencies with five opportunities in your marketplace.

Core Competencies	Opportunities in the Marketplace
1.	1.
2.	2.
3.	3.
4.	4.
5.	5.

#7: Creating a Competitive Advantage

Now that you have identified your unique core competencies and opportunities in your marketplace, it is time to match the two together to create a competitive advantage. Your competitive advantage is an ability to outperform your competition (other trainers or fitness professionals) in providing your services or products.

In August 2006, Ben Rosario and Matt Helbig of Big River Running Company in St. Louis, Missouri, combined their passion for running with an opportunity in the marketplace: the growing niche market of runners wanting personalized shoe-fitting services. Specialty running stores posted sales near $600 million in 2006. That revenue grew 12.4 percent in the first half of 2007, according to a survey published by Leisure Trends Group. In Rosario's words, "If you do it right—and I knew we could—you can build a very loyal customer base. It is a better experience than you'll get online or at a big-box store."

Plenty of individuals will still choose larger athletic shoe retailers because of lower prices, but Rosario and Helbig are not targeting this market. Their market includes a variety of runners—both beginners and seasoned veterans—who want personalized service that will enable them to perform at their best. Big River Running Company also takes the experience outside the store by offering free training sessions, group runs, and education to their customer base; they pay it forward. Rosario and Helbig have since opened a second location in March 2008.

Combining your skills and passion with unrecognized opportunities in your marketplace, or taking something you do extremely well and matching it with a specific need at the right place and right time will generate results. Once word spreads that you are the "go-to" trainer for a specific area of expertise, you will have created an advantage over other trainers in your geographic location.

You have an enormous vault of information to share with your target market, but to make an impact, you need to know what you do better than anyone else. Link those skills to opportunity and you will have created a competitive advantage. Congratulations! You are about to take an important step: defining who you are and what you want your business to become.

Exercise

Using the list of core competencies and opportunities from the previous exercise, list two competitive advantages and how you will use them to develop two new exercise/wellness program concepts you can implement within the next 30 days.

1.

2.

Jupiterimages

#8: SWOT Your Competition

Understanding your strengths and weaknesses is important in terms of setting up your personal training business for success. So is the ability to identify opportunities in the marketplace as well as threats from your competition. When you put these components down on paper, you have performed a SWOT analysis.

The American Marketing Association defines the SWOT analysis, sometimes called a situational analysis, as an examination of the internal factors (strengths and weaknesses) and external factors (opportunities and threats) that affect your business. It may seem silly to perform such a task; after all, you know what you do well, don't you? An easy parallel is the client who maintains that they eat a healthy diet only to have their eyes opened by keeping a food log. Like that client, you may not always look at your strengths and weaknesses objectively. It's also important to identify external opportunities in your marketplace and threats from other fitness facilities or trainers. Following is an example of a SWOT analysis.

Strengths

- Good communication skills
- Develops innovative exercise programs and group classes
- Strong reputation in your target market as the leading weight-loss expert

Weaknesses

- Limited financial resources
- Does not have a website
- Limited marketing skills

Opportunities

- New medical building under construction that will house several new medical practices
- Several parks that attract people from different demographic segments (runners, walkers, moms, seniors)

Threats

- XYZ Personal Training has started a new weight-loss boot camp at the local park three days per week
- Trainers from Get Fit Personal Training have formed alliances with local physicians to offer weight-loss services to their patients

Your goal is simple. First, identify internal strengths/weaknesses and external opportunities and threats. Second, convert your weaknesses to strengths, match your strengths to opportunities in your location, and neutralize threats from competing firms. This analysis will serve as an important basis for developing your business plan.

Exercise

Perform a SWOT Analysis. List three items for every category.

Strengths
1.
2.
3.

Weaknesses
1.
2.
3.

Opportunities
1.
2.
3.

Threats
1.
2.
3.

Match your strengths to opportunities.
1.
2.
3.

Convert your weaknesses to strengths.
1.
2.
3.

Determine how to neutralize threats to your training business.
1.
2.
3.

#9: What Is Your Mission in Life?

Have you asked yourself recently why you are a personal trainer and what your business's purpose is for existing? If not, you should give it some thought. A well-defined mission states what you are and where you want your business to go. A mission refers to an organization's fundamental purpose for existing, defining what the organization is, its values and the customers it wishes to serve (Berkowitz, 2004). Sometimes, this definition is referred to as a mission statement.

The mission statement sets the tone for the organization's philosophy and helps set direction for future business decisions. It asks two questions.
- Who are your customers?
- What do you do better than anyone else?

Chances are likely you became a personal trainer because you have a desire to help people improve their health and wellness. You want to help people lose weight, run a marathon, or simply have more energy to play with their children. Perhaps you also have philanthropic interests, such as Susan G. Komen for the Cure®, the American Heart Association, or the American Red Cross. You also want to make a profit. These factors are the components of a mission statement. One of the best examples of a mission statement comes from a company trainers tell many of their clients to consume in moderation: Ben & Jerry's® ice cream. Table 9-1 displays Ben & Jerry's mission statement.

Ben & Jerry's Mission

Social Mission	Product Mission	Economic Mission
To operate the company in a way that actively recognizes the central role that businesses play in society by initiating innovative ways to improve the quality of life locally, nationally, and internationally.	To make, distribute, and sell the finest quality all-natural ice cream and euphoric concoctions with a continued commitment to incorporating wholesome, natural ingredients and promoting best practices that respect the Earth and the environment.	To operate the company on a sustainable, financial basis of profitable growth, increasing value for our stakeholders and expanding opportunities for development and career growth for our employees.

Source: www.benjerry.com/activism/mission-statement

Table 9-1. Ben & Jerry's mission statement

The firm clearly states its product, economic, and social mission. As a result, Ben & Jerry's stands as a well-respected corporate citizen because of its passion for producing a high quality product, being profitable to benefit both stakeholders and employees, and operating their business in a manner that improves society in general.

Your mission statement does not need flash or pizzazz. It needs to be from the heart and representative of who you are and what you want your business to become. Remember, a training prospect should read your mission statement and get a clear understanding of you, your business, and what you believe in—that they know without a doubt you are their personal trainer.

Exercise

Write a brief mission statement that describes your business. Be sure to include your product, economic philosophy, and social belief. You may want to search the Internet to find good examples of mission statements.

Jupiterimages

#10: What Do You Have to Sell?

Fitness professionals or personal trainers typically "sell" training. However, you can only see a certain number of clients each day no matter how hard you try. Offering one-on-one training only, you will either have to charge an exorbitant fee or spend unrealistic hours training clients. You also have to factor in travel time for in-home clients and down time in between clients. It is possible to make a living in this capacity, but it can be hard to sustain.

Therefore, if you are focused on one-on-one training or are limited in your service or product offering, you may want to consider expanding what you do. The business concept of strategic business units, or SBUs, can help you build a framework in which to expand your business.

Think about an SBU as another division or product line under your main line of business. To build your business and increase revenue, you need to develop different SBUs within your business. You may immediately think of soft drinks when you hear the words "Coca-Cola®." However, the company has expanded over the years to offer bottled water, sports drinks, juices, teas, and coffees.

While one-on-one training can be your core business, open your mind to different ways to service clients to avoid becoming stagnant, and use innovation to fuel your growth. What can you do to enhance your product offering? Table 10-1 provides examples of ways you can expand your product offering that will appeal to a wider target market and increase your revenues.

Personal-Training Services
- One-on-one training
- Small-group training
- In-home training
- Online coaching/program development
- Boot camps or classes

Tangible Goods
- Nutritional supplements
- E-books
- Fitness equipment

Table 10-1. Examples of ways to expand your product line

Remember, you can make more revenue training three people in a small group setting that you can one client at a time. You can also generate passive revenue by selling supplements, equipment, or e-books on your website, which never closes. Think outside the box, and do not limit yourself. By developing different SBUs, you can develop multiple lines of revenue that you can reinvest into growing your business.

Exercise

Break down your product line into two areas: personal training services and tangible goods. Brainstorm as many different SBUs as you can come up with. Then, break them into products that you can implement immediately, in six months and one year from now.

Hemera/Thinkstock

#11: Assessing Your Share

In marketing, the term "market" refers to the individuals or organizations that are interested in a product and who have the ability and authority to purchase that product (Pride and Ferrell, 2008). In the fitness industry, this represents a large and diverse group of individuals and businesses. According to the International Health, Racquet and Sportsclub Association (IHRSA), there were approximately 41.1 million health club members in 2005. It is a safe assumption that as people become more health-conscious, the number of consumers seeking gyms and fitness-related services will continue to increase. What is your share of that 41.1 million? Should you be concerned with knowing your share? If you want your business to grow, the answer is yes.

The American Marketing Association defines "market share" as the proportion of total sales in a market obtained by a facility or business. A key to this definition is "in a market." Stop for a moment to consider the number of fitness facilities and trainers in your geographic area. You can get a good idea just by scanning the Yellow Pages. How much of your potential customer base do each of these facilities or trainers have compared to you? While that may be too broad of a scope to begin with, you can start by determining your share of clients in the facility in which you train.

- Determine the number of members in your facility.
- Determine the number of members in your facility who use personal-training services.
- What is the breakdown of personal trainers compared to the number of clients being trained?

Say there are 500 members in your facility, and of those 500 members, 150 purchase personal training. There are five personal trainers in your club (including yourself), and you are currently training 12 clients. This means you have an 8 percent share of the current market for personal training in your club.

You still have room for growth because there are 350 members in your facility who are personal-training prospects. You could begin by offering something your colleagues don't or won't. Sponsor a free wellness presentation, offer a sports-specific workshop, or develop a new exercise class that will introduce members to you. Pad your resume by obtaining new certifications, skills, and abilities. Submit articles to local newspapers, journals, and magazines. Jump at every opportunity to appear on television, in print, or on the radio as an expert. Expand your market by developing an online product or by marketing your expertise to local businesses looking for ways to cut health-care costs. By becoming visible, you will increase your odds of obtaining more clients and increasing your share of the market in your geographic location. It is impossible to completely dominate the market for personal training, but being in demand and having a waiting list of clients who want to train *only* with you is a wonderful problem to have!

#12: What Are Your Four Ps?—The Marketing Mix

The core of marketing for any business or organization, large or small, is the four Ps. These four Ps make up the marketing mix, or four marketing activities, all businesses perform.

- *Product*: What you intend to sell
- *Price*: How much you will charge for your product
- *Promotion*: How you intend to let your target market know about your product
- *Placement*: How and where your product will be distributed

The four Ps are controllable. If you want to change the way you deliver a service, you can modify the way you conduct a training session. You can raise or lower your prices, train clients in-home, at a gym, or online, and you can place an ad in a local newspaper to advertise your services to your target market.

As personal trainers, your primary product will be your training services, but as you expand your business, your products could include consumable goods such as nutritional supplements. The previous sections have discussed defining what your product or products will be. Next, you need to think about the rest of the equation.

- How much will you charge for your services?
- How will you let your target market know you exist?
- How will you distribute your goods and services?

Each of these aspects of the marketing mix will be explored in detail throughout this book. Outline a marketing mix strategy for every product or good in your product line. Different products will appeal to different customers due to timing, economic conditions, and personal preference. Make sure you have a clear-cut plan that will include a strategy for every product in your arsenal.

Exercise

Develop a marketing mix strategy for every product in your product line. Think about each service or good individually, how you intend to sell it, what you will charge for it, where and how it will be distributed, and how you will let your customers and potential customers know about it. Be sure to think through and clearly define each component.

Product
1.
2.
3.
4.

Price
1.
2.
3.
4.

Placement
1.
2.
3.
4.

Promotion
1.
2.
3.
4.

#13: Who Is Your Market?

When you think about who your customers are, your immediate thought is to pull out your log of customer names. However, the answer is better found in the unique qualities that each of your clients possesses. Look at the qualities that make up this group in terms of age, gender, household income, belief systems, philosophies about health and wellness, lifestyle, and geographic location. You may begin to see a pattern. For example, you may notice that your customers tend to be 40- to 50-year-old men who are passionate about running and healthy eating. They tend to live in a certain type of neighborhood. Perhaps your customers are active, single women age 28 to 40 who desire to maintain the physique they had in college. Whatever pattern emerges will help pinpoint your target market. These similarities can be broken down into three categories: demographics, psychographics, and geographics.

The American Marketing Association defines a target market as the particular segment of a total population on which a business focuses its marketing efforts to meet and satisfy the needs of that market segment. Chances are, if you began to list the individual characteristics of your current client base, you would see a pattern in terms of similarities.

- Demographic segmentation looks at categories such as age, sex, household income, education, occupation, family size, religion, and social class.
- Psychographic segmentation refers to personality, motives, and lifestyle characteristics.
- Geographic segmentation looks at region, city size, market density, and urban versus suburban location.

It's important information to know because marketing can be expensive. Businesses that try to be all things to all people rarely succeed. This does not mean you cannot train different types of clients, but if you find a niche training a particular type of client, become successful at it, and are able to generate more customers in this category, it makes sense to focus your energy on that market segment. For example, you may find the majority of your clientele happen to be Caucasian women age 37 to 50 with an annual household income of $200,000. They also happen to all live within 10 minutes of your facility. The data tell you there is a market for your services in this geographic location. The financial numbers indicate these women have the ability and desire to pay for your services; their motives could be driven by health, aesthetics, or performance.

The bottom line is to know who your clients are, what they want, where they live, and how you can impress upon them that you can help them meet and exceed their objectives better than any other trainer. Of course, you could continue to blindly advertise your services, wasting time and money, or you can learn to identify who your bread-and-butter clients are and develop marketing techniques to push their hot buttons and get more clients. Which option sounds better to you?

Exercise

Determine your target market or markets. Identify demographics, psychographics, and geographics of the target market you plan to market your business.

Demographics
1.
2.
3.

Psychographics
1.
2.
3.

Geographics
1.
2.
3.

#14: The Economic Environment

In marketing, all businesses must pay attention to several environmental factors, and personal trainers are no different. These factors play a major role in how business is conducted and can play a major role in the health of your business.

Most marketing experts will tell you that unlike the four Ps, which are controllable, you cannot do anything to shape these environmental factors. This is partly true. Some businesses will sit back and react to what the environment gives them, while others will be proactive and will make adjustments accordingly to help their business survive and thrive. You always want to take action and be proactive in every situation. The first environmental factor you need to understand is the economic environment.

According to the American Marketing Association, the economic environment encompasses factors such as productivity, income, wealth, inflation, pricing, and employment. It is a combination of these factors that can affect a company and its opportunities. Personal trainers work in a field that is greatly dependent on discretionary income, or the funds that are left after a person pays bills and the basic necessities of life. What that person does with those leftover funds is up to that individual. He may take a vacation, buy a car, or play a round of golf. As a personal trainer, you are attempting to show enough value that a client or potential client will want to spend their leftover funds on you.

Economic and business conditions are cyclical. Like the tides, one can do nothing but press on and adjust to current economic conditions, but trainers can recession-proof their business by being proactive and by paying attention to who they are training and how they run their business.

- *Position yourself as a medical professional*: Position your business as complementary to services such as physicals, chiropractic adjustments, and dental cleanings. Personal trainers help people improve their health and performance and should not be looked upon as a leisure service.
- *Define your target market*: When you developed your target market, did you focus on a demographic whose income is at a level where even in times of recession, they will have the discretionary income to afford your services?
- *Tighten the reigns*: If you experience a slow-down in business, that is the time to do an analysis of where your company spends money. What is your return on investment (ROI) in the advertising you purchased in your local newspaper? Do you need that new exercise-design software, or can you make it a while longer on the older version? Be mindful not only of your revenues, but of your expenses as well.

- *Adjust your pricing*: This part of the four Ps can be changed quite easily. If you are finding resistance with an average hourly rate of $70, you can either reduce your session rates or offer promotions such as buy 10 sessions and get one session free.
- *Pay attention to economic indicators*: It may seem like a foreign language at first but by reading publications such as *BusinessWeek* and the *Wall Street Journal*, you will be on the cutting edge of the state of the economy. You can use this information to recession-proof your business.

While you can do little to change the economic conditions in our society, you can be proactive in adjusting the way you do business to keep your personal-training business healthy. Take aggressive steps to solidify your business in all economic conditions, and you will be one step ahead of your competition.

iStockphoto/Thinkstock

#15: The Competitive Environment

Who are your competitors? If you don't know, you better take note because they are most certainly paying attention to what you are doing. You're not the only player in town. The seemingly abundant number of health and fitness providers has grown in recent years because our society has a greater awareness than ever of health and fitness, coupled with the ease of access to information on what's available.

Competition is part of business. According to the American Marketing Association, the competitive environment includes the number and strength of rival firms competing in the same market for a product. Some businesses compete based on their brand, offering similar products or services at similar prices. For example, Nike®, New Balance®, and Adidas® compete for a share in the running shoes market. Others compete for the same group of customers with different products, such as bottled or canned beverages including Evian® water, Coca-Cola, Gatorade®, and Minute Maid® iced tea. Therefore every gym and personal trainer who trains clients in your geographic area should be considered your competition. Staying ahead of your rivals comes down to being proactive versus reacting to what your competitors are doing.

The first step is to conduct an environmental scan, which comes down to paying attention to the competition and conducting some research. What kind of programs are the trainers in your area offering? How are they marketing themselves? Do they use catchy buzzwords? How do they price their services and products? How do they advertise? Gathering this information is as easy as picking up a phone and asking them about their services, philosophies, and pricing. This tactic is called secret shopping. You should also visit their websites and use search engines to find out where and how they advertise.

Next, position yourself as the local expert. Submit articles to local newspapers, write a blog on your website or Facebook page, and communicate with local media. Let them know who you are and that you are more than willing to serve as the local expert on any fitness and nutrition related story that may come their way. Keep abreast of fitness and wellness trends. Never pass up the chance to be on television, on the radio, or in print. It may seem scary the first time you do it, but there is no better advertising in the world than being the fitness expert on the 10 p.m. news—and it costs you nothing.

Finally, educate yourself. Seek additional degrees or certifications. Read journals, attend conferences, and subscribe to as much information as you can digest. If you are on the cutting edge of your industry, you will always stay one step ahead of your competitors.

Exercise

Perform an environmental scan on the gyms and trainers in your immediate geographic location (within 10 miles of where you conduct business). Take note of the following:

- Advertising methods
- Education and experience
- Program and service offerings
- Pricing
- Anything else that you can use as an advantage to better your business

Medioimages/Photodisc

#16: Capitalizing on Changes in Technology

Technology is all around. In your own lifetime, you have seen an evolution beyond epic proportions, with technological change happening faster than in any other time in history. Advances in technology influence the way you work, shop, and function in everyday life; society is "connected" with cell phones, Wi-Fi connections at the local Internet cafe, podcasts, and more. With technology comes change. Sixty-two million U.S. households, or 55 percent of American homes, had an Internet-connected computer in 2003, according to the latest available U.S. Census data, and according to CTIA-The Wireless Association®, approximately 250 million Americans are now subscribers to some sort of cell-phone plan. That's about 82.5 percent of the U.S. population. These developments are something to which you need to be paying attention.

The American Marketing Association defines technological change as the discovery and application of new products, new and improved machines, tools, equipment, and methods of production. Technological change will continue, and even accelerate, which means discovering new and different ways to reach your target market and to market your products or services in ways you may not have imagined is crucial for growth. So how can you make the most of technological advances? While your business may not be a technologically driven operation, there are many ways for you to capitalize on the advances in technology in your advertising and marketing, client retention efforts, and more. Following are just a few examples that can help you on your way to coming up with even more creative ways to use technology, and the light-speed changes in technology, to expand your health and fitness business.

- Text message appointment reminders to your clients
- Online fitness newsletter
- E-mail exercise tips and programs
- Website
- Online payment (have your clients pay you online along with other online bill pay)
- Blog (short for "weblog") to have online discussions
- Search engine marketing

Being able to send a workout to a client's phone, texting a motivational quip, or improving efficiency by accepting online bill pay is utilizing technology to your advantage. Trends will come, and trends will go, but where you exist when that particular piece of technology is the hottest is a good indicator of where you are as a business owner. It is not necessary to be master of the technological universe, but if you aren't including new technologies in the way you train, you are missing the boat.

#17: Society's Impact on Personal Training

Every day of your life, people and events influence your behavior. A friend recommends a particular exercise class. Another friend is determined to compete in a triathlon. You see an advertisement for a healthy beverage. An aging family member has a health challenge. Each of these events will shape your thoughts and behaviors. You may try that new class, decide to train for a triathlon, buy the healthy beverage, or take up a cause the supports research into the family member's health challenge.

These influences, or sociocultural forces, bring about change in the thoughts and behaviors, and can have a tremendous impact of what, where, how, and when people choose and purchase services and products. And it will affect how you, as a business owner or personal trainer, look at the market in which you do business. Look at it as an opportunity to expand your perspective on who your customers are today and can be in the future.

One such influence is the demographic makeup of the population. More and more baby boomers are concerned with maintaining their health well into their retirement. Another influence, which can evolve slowly but have profound effect on a large population, is cultural value. Think about how health, nutrition, and exercise have taken root in American culture. They've become mainstream, a way of life, for many Americans. In the not-so-distant past, quick and easy (think microwave dinners in a cardboard box or instant meals in a can) far outweighed balanced health. Everything from your political views to how you chose health care has its roots in the sociocultural environment.

Consideration of these sociocultural factors might help you to look outside your current customer base and consider changing or expanding your target market. The second aspect of this environment is to look at how other people make decisions based upon where they come from and how they were raised. There's an entire market of individuals out there who want health and fitness services. Your job is to understand how to best position your business to serve their needs and then present it is a fashion that is appealing to how they see the world. Figure that out, and you will be way ahead of the curve.

#18: Legal and Regulatory Considerations

Going hand in hand with ethics is the legal and regulatory environment in which all business operate. Guidelines and laws are designed to protect you, consumers, and other businesses (or your competitors) regarding advertising and marketing to consumers. You should be familiar with a few areas for your own protection.

Simply put, it's in your best interest to be truthful about the products and services you offer. Consumers have rights to protect themselves from actual and potential physical harm caused by misrepresentation or mislabeling of a product. They also have protection from false advertisement, false representation of a product or service, and deceptive selling methods, such as bait and switch. So when you advertise or market your business or services, be completely truthful.

Companies have protection under federal law to protect their logo, trademark, names, and other registered symbols. In a nutshell, you can't fashion your logo after another or name your business Gary's Gold's Gym®. Be sure to check that your logo or tagline isn't identical or very similar to a competitor's or any other business's logo.

It's typically good business practice to apply for accreditation by your local Better Business Bureau (BBB). The BBB is a non-government regulatory agency supported by local businesses. It will help settle problems that arise between consumers and businesses, and will also list whether there are complaints against businesses. It will also let your customers and prospects know you are an honest business person. To find out more, visit www.bbb.org.

Finally, legislation can change the way you do business in the drop of a hat. More and more regulation in the nutritional supplement industry occurs every day, and some states have considered licensure for personal trainers. It behooves you to stay abreast of what is happening in your state that can affect your business. Something as simple as a letter to your elected official about new legislation can make or break how you do business.

#19: The Marketing Plan—Going From Where You Are to Where You Want to Be

Most people have been on job interviews at which the interviewer asks, "Where do you want to be in five years?" It can be a difficult question to answer if you've never thought about it. But when preparing for a job interview, you likely spent some time on this very question.

It's no different, and perhaps even more important, being in business for yourself. Where do you envision yourself, your business, in one year, in five years? That vision is the basis for your marketing plan, the detailed written document that's the journey taking you from where you are to where you want to be. It can be a simple, one-page document to a complex, multipage package that includes matrixes and timelines.

Any good marketing plan should include the following elements. Some of this information you've already gathered in previous sections. It's a matter of putting it together.

- The mission of your company: why you are in business
- A brand promise: what you plan to deliver, including a strong message or two that will be consistent in your marketing efforts
- A product definition: exactly what product or service you offer
- The competition: who you are competing against for your defined target market
- Target market: exactly who you want to sell your services to
- Your goals/objectives: what you are trying to accomplish
- Strategies: how you plan to reach your goals and objectives (For instance, a strategy could be to increase the number of personal-training visits per customer by six per year.)
- Tactics: which pieces of the marketing mix you will use to carry out your strategies (personal selling, online monthly newsletter, and networking)
- Marketing budget: how much you've determined you are able to spend annually
- Strengths, or points of differentiation
- Weaknesses, such as location
- Threats: factors that hinder your success, such as price, location, or quality

Having a solid marketing plan for a defined period, such as a year, will help serve as a reminder of where you are and where you want to be. It's a snapshot that will evolve over time, but is something you can always come back to reference.

For free, template marketing plans, go online and search the term "marketing plans." A couple great reference sites are Ducttapemarketing.com and Marketitright.com.

2

Product—It's More Than What You're Selling

Jupiterimages

#20: Defining Your Product

So you think you're special when it comes to training? Truthfully, any trainer can assign exercises (some better than others) and count reps, so with a multitude of trainers to choose from, defining yourself will help a prospect pick you. The trick is defining your product so you create a wide chasm between you and your competition in the eyes of your prospects.

First and foremost, put your own *individual* stamp on your personal-training business. What is your fitness philosophy, creed, or vision by which you train your clients? If you are unsure what that means, start reading trainer bios on your competition's websites. Everyone says things like "My clients are my number-one priority" and "We build personalized programs," blah, blah, blah. They all sound the same, so what sets you apart? In the sales phase of your business, this is referred to as your "shtick" or your pitch to a prospective client that will set you apart from other trainers. Your philosophy is your core belief about fitness and nutrition, and it should be the platform from which you drive your marketing efforts.

Another way to look at this is through product differentiation. Product differentiation is creating and designing products so customers perceive them as different from competing products (Pride and Ferrell, 2008). Two scenarios can be used to illustrate the difference. Trainer #1 meets with client A two times per week for 45 minutes each session. In that session, Trainer #1 pushes his client to get the most out of his session, educates him on proper form, and motivates him to work on his own until their next session. Trainer #2 meets with client B and performs the same routine as Trainer #1, but the service does not stop there. Not only does she e-mail client B a copy of their session complete with instructions, she calls (not e-mails) her client within 24 hours to check on how they are doing. This is called "adding value to a service," and it differentiates the delivery of the product between the two competing trainers. Who would you rather train with: Trainer #1, who ends his involvement with his clients at the door of the gym, or Trainer #2, who provides service to her clients beyond the four walls of the gym? Living in a market where consumers want the most bang for their buck, the answer is simple.

#21: Creating Your Product Mix

Personal trainers may think of their product line as a single product: training, with a little educating, motivating, and providing hope thrown in. It's why you went to school or became certified. However, if you intend to grow your business and become financially sound, the adage of "thinking outside the box" should be your mantra. Developing a mix of services or products will help sustain you through those lean times when business is slow and you have just one or two clients on a certain day.

The American Marketing Association defines a product mix as the full set of products offered for sale by a business. It includes all product lines and categories. For example, if you offer one-on-one personal training services in single, 5- and 10-pack sessions, you have a very narrow and short product mix. If you also offer group training, online training, corporate wellness, and nutritional products, your business has a wide product mix and more options to generate revenue. Plus, your days will be a lot more fun since you will have a wider array of services to perform.

Developing more than one product or service accomplishes a couple things. First, to meet the needs of a diverse and dynamic target market, you need to have products and services that appeal to a wide variety of personalities and price tolerances. Boxing yourself in to only a single set of services makes you less attractive than the trainer who can be a one-stop shop to his clients and address all of their health and nutrition needs.

Second, trainers who only offer one-on-one sessions don't make money when they don't work, so if they get sick and go on vacation, they generate zero revenue. By developing services such as online training or coaching and offering a line of consumable nutritional products, you can create a solid revenue stream for your business no matter what time of day it is. Imagine a customer ordering protein powder from your website while you sleep. You could also create an e-book based upon your philosophies and teaching style that can be marketed online. Not everyone can afford one-on-one training, but many people will part with $14.99 to download your information. So think outside the box, and use that vision to create ideas beyond the traditional models of personal training to solidify and grow your business.

#22: Product Positioning

The perception you want your customers to have of you, your personal training business, and the products you provide is the basis for the concept of product positioning, and it is important depending on to whom you are marketing your services.

Gold's Gym and Curves® both help people get in shape, lose weight, and improve their overall health, but they cater to two totally different market segments. At Gold's, you are likely to see young professionals, both guys and gals, age 20 to 40, who are looking for more than just a place to work out; they are looking for a relatively inexpensive facility where they can get fit and socialize in a fun atmosphere. Curves, on the other hand, caters only to women. No men allowed. Their product is creating a quick, inexpensive circuit workout that gets clients in and out the door in 30 minutes. This works for busy professionals, moms, and individuals who wouldn't venture into a gym filled with hard bodies. So while both businesses help people get fit, they have positioned themselves to two totally different markets.

Knowing who you will market to is crucial. If you want to market to the upper-income segment in your geographic area, you want your marketing mix to deliver the perception of exclusivity, luxury, and quality. If you run boot camps, the idea is to get as many bodies through the door so your classes are filled. In that case, you might position your class to promote quality experience and discount while creating a perception of value.

Whatever you choose, don't send mixed messages. Create the perception of your product. As you will see later in this book, product positioning will be crucial to building your brand.

Barry Austin

#23: Finding Your Niche

Business owners in any industry who try to be all things to all people typically fail at satisfying the needs of their customers. They simply cannot cover the wants, needs, and desires of an entire population. The fitness industry is no different. When you think about the range of health and wellness services, including weight management, sports-specific training, special populations (youth, geriatric, and special-needs clients), disease management (cardiac and pulmonary rehabilitation), bodybuilding, and the list goes on, you'll soon discover that you can't be all things to all people. So, find your niche.

Finding your niche is as simple as choosing a specific subset of a population on which to focus your training and marketing efforts. If the trainer down the street has cornered the market on endurance athletes, perhaps you should focus on weight-management clients. Alison Thietje, founder of Motion Memory Golf, has created a niche market by working only with high-level amateur and professional golfers. Alison took her passion for golf, identified a need, and created a personal training business that caters to meeting those needs.

Figure out exactly where your strengths and passion lie. Be sure there is a need within your market that can benefit from your services. Then, focus your efforts on developing your business around the specific type of clients you want to serve and you've got yourself a niche market.

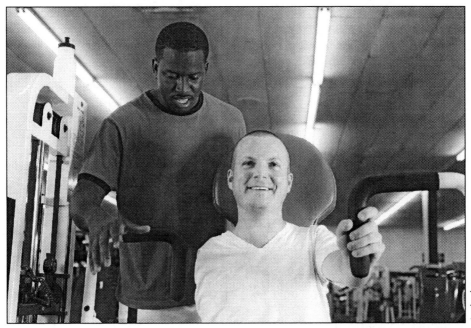

Jupiterimages

#24: Evolving Your Product Line

The most popular concept of personal training is as old as a fossilized tyrannosaurus rex: time for money. A client pays you a fee. You train that client, and then move on to the next paying customer. A great deal, right? Wrong, because, like the dinosaur, this concept will cause your business to go extinct.

To create a dynamic business that stays ahead of the competition, consider these two marketing concepts to evolve your service line: product modifications and line extensions.

- Product modifications are changes to a current product or service. A good example is in the automobile industry. You can buy a brand-new current model year Ford Mustang, but you can't buy brand-new 1998 Mustangs because Ford has modified and improved it. As a personal trainer, you should be modifying and improving your services, too. Perhaps you can offer an online component to your one-on-one services. Help your clients remember what they did in their sessions with an online program complete with pictures and descriptions. Adding depth and value to your product or service can add depth to your bottom line (hint: increase your fees).

- A line extension is developing a service that closely resembles an existing service. Extend your services to offer group training, classes, and boot camps in addition to your one-on-one training sessions. While you may charge $75 per hour for one client, you can charge $35 per client in a group personal-training session with three participants. It provides clients with an economical solution to one-on-one training and you gross $105 per hour instead.

Don't fall victim to extinct ways of thinking and suffer the fate of the T-Rex. Evolve your personal training business and open the doors to a new set of clients.

iStockphoto/Thinkstock

#25: Product Deletion

When a product has run its course and is either no longer financially viable or is costing you money, it may be time to cut it loose. It happens all the time in business.

This may be hard for you, kind of like getting rid of a favorite t-shirt past its prime, but it is something you need to do to be profitable. The good news is that unless you sell supplements and/or exercise equipment, your personal-training services are intangible, so deleting a service won't cause you to lose money. If you are stuck with 100 units of protein powder you can't move, consider a loss-leader sale. For example, every client who signs up for training in April gets a bottle of whey protein for only $20 (hint: sell it for what you purchased it for to recover your costs). Or go lower if you have to. Just get rid of it!

To delete a product, simply take it off your website, brochures, and marketing material. It doesn't mean you have to scrap the idea forever. That same product may make you a revenue-generating machine in the future. The hardest part is identifying the drain on your resources and then having the courage to do something about it. Remember, you are here to help people improve their health, but you're not volunteering your time. If a product is costing you more green than you are bringing in, dump it!

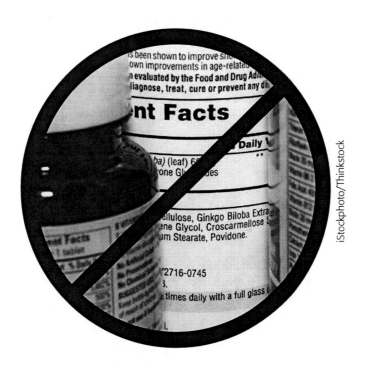

iStockphoto/Thinkstock

#26: Building Your Brand

When you see the golden arches, you don't need to be told there is a McDonald's nearby. You just know. Those golden arches are a brand mark that let's you know exactly what to expect when you pull into the drive-thru. You don't have to worry about variation in texture or taste. That image tells you all you need to know. That is the power of branding.

Brand recognition has a power that money cannot buy. Mention the name Bob Harper to anyone on the street, and that person may not know who you are talking about. Mention the television show *The Biggest Loser* and "Bob the trainer," and people will know who you are talking about. People identify with strong brands. It is why they will choose a more expensive brand at the grocery store over a less expensive store brand. It's also why someone will plunk down large sums of money to work with a celebrity trainer like Bob Harper. There is perceived quality in a well-groomed brand.

To develop your brand, you must first figure out who and what you are. Look back at your mission statement, and use that as a driving force behind how you want your target market to perceive your business. Then, start building the brand by doing things such as the following:

- *Name your business*: Try to be more creative than "Personal Training by Jeremy." Find a name that rolls off the tongue.
- *Develop a logo*: Just as a memorable logo such as the golden arches can stand alone without the McDonald's name, your logo should be able to tell your followers who you are.
- *Hone your "stage" personality*: Whether you are shy or the class clown, try to exert some consistency in your training personality. Why? Because the client who raves about your outgoing personality or your serious demeanor will refer friends who have similar likes. That potential new client may be disappointed if you're the opposite of what their friend described.
- *Uphold your image at all times*: Once people know your brand, be on your toes because your image will follow you wherever you go. Even when you are on your own time, if you plan to cut loose some evening, remember that a client could be watching.

Once you have your brand identified, nurture it as you would a child. Protect it and help it grow. If you do it right, it may be the most important marketing tool you will ever use.

#27: Who Are You?

It's insane to think that clients will continually purchase sessions with inept trainers, but it happens all the time. The reason clients keep going back is that the trainer has done a good job branding himself as a quality trainer and, therefore, there is a perception of quality. Perhaps the trainer has an exiting, engaging personality or maybe a great physique. Sadly, many dollars have been spent on trainers with great physiques and little knowledge. Why? Clients think that the trainer with Olympian-like bodies must know what they are doing and can help them achieve the same results. What is important to you for your personal-training business is building your brand based on your knowledge and expertise so people identify you with a level of quality that is based on your knowledge and expertise, even if you don't have the physique of Mr. or Ms. Olympia.

Quality is in the eye of the beholder. Some may see an economical, fuel-efficient car as a quality automobile, while others need an eight-cylinder gas-guzzling sports machine to satisfy their needs. How people identify with your brand starts with you and the groundwork you lay one customer at a time. Think about how you structure your sessions, what your clients are getting for their money, and your appearance. All of these factors need to be considered when building a brand as discussed in previous sections. Getting your target market to identify your brand as a quality investment will take time.

Your target market will be key in building your brand value. Perhaps your market is high-end clients who will be able to afford you even in down economic times. If so, then build your brand based on the exclusivity and price of your services, but be sure that you live, breathe, and project that image while delivering results. If you are targeting stay-at-home moms who are dragging themselves out of bed at 6 a.m. every morning for boot camps, you certainly don't want to show up with perfect hair, make-up, and nails, because in most cases, they won't either.

Consumers identify with brands because of certain aspects and qualities. Once your clients identify your brand as a quality service and a worthwhile investment for their time and money, you'll be the trainer they keep coming back to for quality results.

#28: How Valuable Is Your Brand?

As stated previously, you are the brand. Personal trainers, homebuilders, and tax preparers build their reputations, or brands, on the level and quality of service they provide. Nurturing and growing your brand increases your perceived value from the groups that matter most: current and prospective clients. To determine the value of your brand, consider the following four components of brand value:

- *Brand awareness*: Being aware of a brand leads to familiarity. The popularity of the reality TV show *The Biggest Loser* has spawned books, workout DVDs, and a number of opportunities for the trainers on the program. Ask yourself: "Is my target market aware of my brand?"

- *Brand loyalty*: Once you get a customer, you want to keep them. Fitness service consumption is not like buying a different brand of paper towels when it's on sale only to return to the original brand once the sale is over. Typically, the relationship last much longer. Ask yourself: "Are my customers staying with me?"

- *Perceived quality*: People are willing to spend more money on brands they perceive to be better. Ask yourself: "What does my reputation tell prospects about my brand?"

- *Brand associations*: Consumers make purchases based on associations. A certain group of people associate Richard Simmons not only with weight loss, but with high energy, empathy, and understanding. Ask yourself: "What emotional response do I want my brand to elicit—an emotional response, or an image of strength, vitality, and energy?"

The dollar amount of a brand is hard to determine. Most businesses, large and small, cannot put an exact value on their brand. Yet it's easy to conclude that the Gold's Gym brand is worth millions, although its success didn't happen overnight. It will take years of work and vigilance to build equity in your brand name, so feed and protect it at all costs.

#29: Co-Branding for Success

Building your own brand is important. Having the opportunity to piggyback on an established brand or business is another way to build your brand—with the help of another.

Co-branding is using two or more brands on one product. Credit-card companies and airlines are a good example of co-branding, with the ability to gain frequent-flier miles through credit card use. Real-estate agents team up with mortgage lenders, title companies, handyman services, and home inspectors to offer solutions for their clients. Translating the concept to your personal-training business can be as easy as pairing convenience and one-stop shopping. Many products and services can go hand-in-hand with personal training, such as massage therapy, nutrition counseling, or chiropractic medicine. Team up with another profession to offer your clients all they need to improve their health, lose weight, and feel great.

To get started co-branding your services, find a massage therapist, dietitian, or other health-care professional who you trust and who has similar philosophies. Discuss how you will combine your products and services, set a price structure, and hammer out logistics. It will also serve you and your partners well to create a legal agreement so there are no stones left unturned when creating your co-brand.

The trainer who continues to think up new ways to package the same products and services wins at the end of the day. Clients want convenience, service, and results. By co-branding, you can do all of these and more.

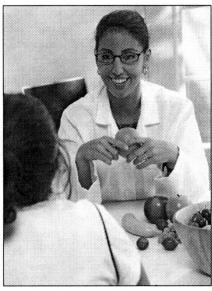

Liquidlibrary

#30: Bob's Personal Training— Selecting a Brand Name

Bob's Personal Training could be your business name if your name is Bob and you are a personal trainer. However, it's boring. The name has no substance, no pizzazz, nothing that grabs attention of consumers or differentiates this personal-training business from any other.

Your business name and how you brand it is more important than you think. Businesses pay consultants millions of dollars to come up with catchy, attention-grabbing brand names that will reflect the true nature of the product or service. But unless you have millions to spend, it's up to you to think about how you want people to perceive your brand. Who are you? What do you stand for? What are your philosophies? How do you see yourself and your business? What kind of mark or symbol might best represent who and what you are?

The laundry detergent brand all® suggests that no stain is too powerful. The insurance company Allstate® uses the brand mark of two hands cupped together along with the tagline "You're in good hands with Allstate®" to instill trust and confidence. McDonald's has its unmistakable golden arches. The brand and name are very important.

Sit down with a notepad, and start jotting names. Again, think about what you are and what you want your brand name to mean to you, your customers, and prospects. Bounce ideas off family and friends. Is it catchy? Does it grab their attention? Look at your competition and their company names or brand marks. Next, look into hiring a graphic designer to help you create a logo. If it's not in your budget, find a designer who's willing to trade design services for training sessions. Or look contact a local university; starving college students work for less.

If you already have a business and brand name or logo, don't worry about changing them. Businesses do it all the time. The most important thing is to create the right brand name. When you get it, you will know. Then relaunch it with a bang.

#31: Protecting Your Investment

It makes zero sense to invest time and money in developing a brand, a brand mark, or logo and then not take the necessary steps to protect it. Creating the perfect brand name and logo only to see it stolen and trademarked by a competitor can kill your business.

Protecting your investment should be a priority. There are two critical steps to protecting your brand: hiring an attorney and hiring an accountant. You'll incur additional expenses, but you will be thankful.

- *Hiring an attorney*: An attorney will help you trademark your name and logo. Find one that specializes in trademark and patent law, and ask him to explain the process to you. You can do it yourself and save money by visiting the U.S. Patent and Trademark Office website (www.uspto.gov) and follow the step-by-step guide. However, it is a complicated process, so you'll want to ask an attorney to review what you've done.

- *Hiring an accountant*: An accountant will do more than tally your tax returns at the end of the year; he can help you register your business name with the state you reside in, and advise you of the tax advantages of incorporating, establishing a limited liability corporation, or taking on a business partner.

When done right, filing for a trademark or registering your business as a specific entity does not take a tremendous amount of time, but it needs to be done right the first time. It will protect your brand name and intellectual properties from competitors and will give you peace of mind.

Hemera/Thinkstock

#32: Making the Intangible Tangible

Unless you include exercise equipment, supplements, or apparel in your product line, what you sell is intangible. Your clients are purchasing your time and expertise when you perform a training session. They leave the session with the physical effects of the workout, the knowledge gained, and a printed copy of their workout.

To create an edge over your competition, you have to provide more than the workout itself. You have to find ways to make the intangible tangible.

First, look at your marketing tools. Marketing your services forces you to give the prospect enough visual information so they can actually see themselves working with you. Help paint the picture by featuring shots of you, your clients (just make sure to get their permission), and your studio to illustrate what prospects may experience spending time with you.

Second, increase the quality of your office supplies. Print workouts, meal plans, and exercise descriptions on high-quality paper. Bind it rather than staple it. Think back to the section on service quality; this is raising the bar and providing service that exceeds expectation.

Finally, give them something tangible. Add value by throwing in a bottle of water, a ready-to-go protein shake, or a t-shirt. Build these things into the price of your session if you prefer. The client won't know unless you tell them, and you can say these "tangible" items are inclusive to your service. It will "wow" them and make each of your customers feel special.

iStockphoto/Thinkstock

#33: Product Life Cycle

All products and services move through a life cycle of introduction, growth, maturity, and decline. A high-profile example was Apple's launch of the iPhone®. When it was introduced in January 2007, consumers lined up for hours to have the chance to own the latest and newest all-in-one gadget. The iPhone had no competitors, and it was the hot item.

Since that time, there have been newer, updated versions of the iPhone, competing products have entered the market, and it has moved into the growth cycle. Eventually, the market will saturate, the demand for the iPhone will mature, decline, and eventually, the iPhone as you know it today will be phased out.

With personal training, you should think about how your services are impacted by the product life-cycle concept. Being knowledgeable about the latest trends and science in exercise and fitness is crucial. When you learn something new or come across a new concept in a journal (or while attending a conference), you have an opportunity to be the first in your market to introduce a new product, service, or technique. Being innovative and creative will help keep your clients and prospects interested in exercise and your personal training services.

As a fitness trend moves through the life cycle, you can determine if it is worth your time and energy to continue offering it. If it isn't making you money—or worse, if it's costing you money—move on. Don't worry if you really liked that product or service. Many trends are cyclical and will eventually work themselves back to being the hot trend.

Who would have guessed a simple exercise from your grade school gym class—push-ups—would become a staple of the hottest thing going: boot camps. Understand where your services or products lie in the life cycle and what your clients want, and be savvy enough to know when a product truly has entered its golden years. Don't be afraid to walk away from it.

3

Price—Deciding How Much to Charge

Creatas

#34: Pricing Decisions

Another "P" of the marketing mix is price. Deciding how your product or service is priced will help to determine your customer base (who can or cannot afford what you offer) and how your product or service is perceived (premium pricing can translate into a perception of high quality or status). It's not as simple as picking the price your competitor charges. Your pricing decision will depend on a number of factors, from location to competition to the economy.

The following exercise is designed to get you thinking about your prices relative to a number of factors. Businesses large and small make pricing decisions every day. Even if you already have your prices set, it's good to evaluate the pricing structure on a regular basis. You may end up confirming what you already knew or deciding that you need to completely revise your pricing.

Exercise

Answer the following questions to the best of your ability. It may take some research and, in some cases, a good hard look at yourself.

- Who are your customers?
- Who do you want your customers to be?
- What are your competitors charging?
- Is your pricing higher, lower, or about the same as your competitors?
- What do you need to charge to break even (after paying yourself), make money to reinvest in your business, and give yourself a raise each year?
- Have you raised your prices?
- When did you last raise your prices?
- What's the economy like?
- How's the economy affecting your clientele?
- How's the economy affecting your own livelihood?

#35: Pricing Objectives

Before you decide what prices to charge, it's important to set objectives on what you want to accomplish with your pricing. Pricing has to be set with your overall business objectives in mind, as well as what you hope to accomplish with your product or service, whether it's to make the world a healthier place or to train elite runners.

You also have to keep in mind what consumers are willing to pay. A can of Coke is about $0.75. With the number of convenient soft-drink and beverage choices available to consumers, it's unlikely that Coca-Cola would consider raising the price of a can of Coke to $5.

The Coke example is a simple one, but it illustrates the importance of pricing a product or service and determining whether that price will meet one or several objectives. Some common pricing objectives to consider include the following:

- *Increase sales*: More sales can translate to more income.
- *Make immediate profits*: Businesses that are relatively new may need to recoup start-up costs.
- *Maximize profits in the short term or long term*: Short-term objectives are likely very different than long-term objectives
- *Break even*: A new business owner with overhead may strive to break even versus losing money in the first year.
- *Beat competitor pricing*: Pricing below the competitor may sway your competitors' customers to try your business.
- *Enhance the image of your business*: Higher prices may elicit an image of quality.
- *Expand your business*: Offer more services or locations to appeal to a wider audience.
- *Increase market share*: A lower price in the short run may entice another trainer's clients to try your services.
- *Maintain customer loyalty*: Long-term customers may be loyal but sometimes need a reason to not try the competition.
- *Differentiate your product or service*: What makes your product or service stand out can be a reflection of price.
- *Survive*: When there's a downturn in the economy or your business is just not where you want it to be, pricing may be a matter of survival.

Strategy and Tactics of Pricing: A Guide to Profitable Decision Making and *Pricing for Profitability: Activity-Based Pricing for Competitive Advantage* are two books that can help when deciding pricing objectives for your company.

#36: Setting Prices

Now that you have an idea of your objectives and have knowledge about pricing decisions, it's time to set your prices for your personal-training business. Remember, you have to cover your costs and make a living.

Armed with knowledge, pricing is still a tricky business. About.com: Entrepreneurs (http://entrepreneurs.about.com/) outlines four ways to set prices: cost-plus pricing, target return pricing, value-based pricing, and psychological pricing.

- *Cost-plus pricing*: Set the price at your cost plus a certain profit margin. Say you do personal training, and you have an agreement with a fitness facility to use their space. You'll need to factor in the cost of travel, your salary, and what you are paying the gym.
- *Target return pricing*: Set your price to achieve a target return-on-investment (ROI). Say you have $15,000 invested in the company, and you want to recoup all your investment in the first year. You'll need to set your prices with a certain margin that targets getting that investment back. How many $75 sessions do you need to recoup your investment?
- *Value-based pricing*: Price your product based on the value it creates for the customer. Value-base pricing can be very profitable, if you can achieve it.
- *Psychological pricing*: Take into consideration the consumer's perception of your price as follows:
  - ✓ Positioning: If you want to signal high quality, you should price your services higher than most of your competition.
  - ✓ Popular price points: At certain price points, or specific prices, people become much more willing to buy things. Common price points are $19.95 or value meals for under $5. Dropping your price to a popular price point might mean a lower margin but more than enough increase in sales to offset it.
  - ✓ Fair pricing: Sometimes it simply doesn't matter what the value of the product is, even if you don't have any direct competition. There is simply a limit to what consumers perceive as "fair."

Regardless of the pricing method or combination of methods you choose, know your market and what they are willing and able to pay, while building in a margin to ensure you make a profit. You can also utilize components of the promotion mix. Plan specials, promotions, and special offers to take advantage of the hot times of the year (New Year's resolutions) and slower periods (summertime).

#37: Price Discounting

Knowing that consumers make buying decisions based on quality, benefits, and advantages of a product or service, you may want to offer discounts at certain times. A new competitor entering the market, an economic downturn, or a new training studio around the corner stepping up its advertising efforts may warrant a short-term business decision such as a discount or sale.

Discounting prices can result in attracting new customers, maintaining current customers, or enticing existing clients to try something new. Types of discounts you may consider include the following:

- *Seasonal discounts*: Summer can be a slow time for a trainer. Stimulate demand by offering a training special in July.
- *Quantity discounts*: Offering discounts for purchasing personal training or supplements in quantities. This works great for selling large packages (20+ sessions).
- *Coupons*: Offering a percentage off or discount with a coupon used in an advertisement—either online or in print. Using coupons also enables you to measure the effectiveness of your ad (how many coupons are actually used).
- *Bundles*: Link together multiple products at a discounted rate. Link a 10 pack of training sessions with a massage and a tub of protein powder to create value and a one-stop-shop appeal.
- *Reward points*: With reward systems, consumers receive a specified amount of points for every dollar spent. The points accumulate until the customer has enough to redeem for benefits. Such practices are common with airlines and credit cards but can easily be used for other products or services. Once a client has reached a certain level, give them a free session, a massage, or something they will find valuable. It will increase loyalty and is good relationship management.

Be sure that when offering discounts you still cover your costs of doing business.

#38: Competitor Pricing

The guy down the street is charging $10 per session more than you, and the woman around the corner is charging $10 less. It's the conundrum all business owners face—just when you've set a price, someone comes in lower and steals your clients, while another establishes a higher price in an attempt to create an image of prestige. You've just stepped into the world of competitor-based pricing. Prices are set on the basis of prices charged by competitors.

Pricing, regardless of how it's set, is an important component to sales success. With that in mind, you need to be monitoring the pricing of products and services in your industry. It's fairly easy to check the prices of competitors in person or online. What you do with that information will shape your own competitive pricing strategy.

Factors that have an impact on competitive pricing include the following:
- *Direct competition*: You could end up in a price war you cannot sustain if you lower your prices every time the competitors do.
- *Demographics of your customers*: Most industries have a price range based on the demographic group they target. For example, if your business is geared toward college athletes, your prices need to fall at a lower range than if you are targeting upscale clientele. Stay competitive within the price range for your demographic group.
- *Your industry*: The latest fitness techniques and products can change an industry very quickly. If you fall behind, your prices could be affected. Therefore, keeping up with the industry will benefit your ability to maintain competitive prices.
- *Customer service*: Your customer service, or lack thereof, will allow you to price above or below the competition.

The bottom line is that you must continue to monitor prices to stay competitive. Trade shows, conferences, and industry associations are good places to gather price information, as well as the latest industry trends to keep you a step ahead of the competition.

#39: Positioning From a Pricing Standpoint

In #22, product positioning was presented as who you are targeting, using the example of Curves versus Gold's Gym. You want your target market to be able to differentiate your services from the competition. Without differentiation, you may end up competing solely on the price you charge compared to the competition. That can be a tough position to sustain over the long run.

Another way to position yourself is through pricing, not based on what your competition is charging, but on the value of your services. The price point you set for your services will further define your value to potential clients.

There are several ways you can differentiate yourself that will provide value beyond the competition, and therefore enable you to command a higher price:

- *Take on a leadership position in your market by staying a step or two ahead of the competition.* Be on the cutting edge of knowledge and fitness trends, and bring that value to your customers before your competitors do. A great way to do this is to attend conferences and immediately implement what you learn.
- *Offer customized solutions.* Even if you have a niche market of customers, customizing a program for each of them will bring added value.
- *Identify add-on services you can offer that meet the needs of the market in new ways.* Become the one-stop shop your clients are looking for, and either through your own business or through activities such as co-branding, be the personal-training business than can meet all the needs of your clients from exercise design to nutritional counseling.

It's always important to remember to evaluate your competition thoroughly to ensure that you truly are offering services that will provide the differentiation you need to position yourself at a higher price and greater value. It will be time well spent.

#40: Determining Value in Your Pricing

As you've probably learned, there are many different ways to determine how to price your personal-training services. One of the most common methods is to determine your cost and add some mark-up to generate a profit. Pricing your services can be a tricky business, and no single way is correct. Sometimes, you may look at what others trainers are charging in your market area and set your prices comparably. Another way to price is by determining what the value is that clients place on your services or estimate how much value a service will provide to the buyer, then basing its price on that value. This is the concept of value-based pricing.

Value-based pricing can be a lucrative way to increase your revenues, but there has to be a perceived value in your services, above and beyond the perceived value of your competitors. Think about it this way: say you train one high-profile client, someone who happens to be a good friend but also is known in the community. Potential clients will place a value on the fact that you are training someone well-known. Therefore, clients may be willing to pay more for your services because you are training a local celebrity. It adds the perception of exclusivity.

Your goal should be to avoid setting prices that are either too high, resulting in driving many customers away, or too low, resulting in customers placing a lower value on your training services. Either way, it's a delicate balance that you will find changes over time. As always, listen to the needs of your customers, and the pricing will come.

4

Promotion—Getting the Word Out

Brand X Pictures

#41: Hey, Look at Me!—Promotion Decisions

Take a few minutes to think about the multiple channels, or ways, you encounter advertising about your favorite brands (you name it: shoes, computers, cell-phone providers). Companies market to consumers on billboards, TV, magazines, websites, direct mail, and radio, as well as through direct selling and public relations, to name a few. These ads, or production promotion, are not by any means random. They are thoughtfully planned by the marketer as part of an integrated marketing communications effort. These efforts help ensure that the target market of consumers receives consistent messages about the benefits of the product or service the company offers.

The American Marketing Association defines integrated marketing communications as a planning process designed to ensure that all brand contacts received by a customer or prospect for a product, service, or organization are relevant to that person and consistent over time. Promotion—one of the four Ps of marketing—comes into play here, and it is the part of the marketing mix in which you are telling your target market, "Hey, look at me!"

It makes sense. Consider Allstate Insurance, which competes with other insurance companies. Its marketing communications and tagline ("You're in good hands with Allstate") are consistent and memorable, reflecting Allstate's core values: caring, integrity, initiative, and innovation. In a few words, Allstate shares important information and thereby promotes its insurance products.

Promotional efforts run the gamut, from a large corporation spending millions of dollars on a celebrity spokesperson to the owner of a one-person enterprise handing out business cards. According to Pride and Ferrell (2008), regardless of the dollar amount, promotion will help you:
- Inform your target market that you exist.
- Stimulate demand for your services.
- Encourage prospects to try your product or services.
- Identify prospects.
- Build a loyal customer base.
- Reduce sales fluctuations, especially in tough economic times.

If you are new to the world of personal training or are striking out on your own for the first time, the lure of purchasing fancy ads, TV or radio time, or canvassing neighborhoods with direct-mail pieces can be very sexy, but you would be wise to understand all the nuances of promotion and what kind of return on investment (ROI) you will get for your efforts before running out and opening your checkbook. As a small business, that could be a costly mistake. The following sections will explore the different aspects of promotion—advertising, personal selling, public relations, and sales promotion—and will help you to think through the best mix to help you reach your marketing objectives.

#42: Advertising

Advertising is the most recognizable element of the promotion mix. We see it all the time: TV, Internet, billboards, magazines, newspaper, direct mail, newsletters, and even on public transit. Most companies do some sort of paid advertising to inform and persuade people about the products and services offered, the price, and the qualities of those products.

Advertising can be a cost-effective way to reach large numbers of people, if that's what you want to achieve. You also can reach a very select group of people via targeted advertising. Whatever your goal, it's important to know your target audience and how best to reach them. Advertising can be as individual as specific client mailings or as general as sending postcards to an entire ZIP code. Doing a little homework ahead of time will help you spend your advertising dollars wisely. As an independent personal trainer or studio owner, understanding these concepts and setting an advertising budget is paramount to your success.

Questions to Consider Regarding Your Target Audience

- Who exactly is your target audience? Do you want to reach a certain demographic, such as baby boomers or stay-at-home moms?
- What do they read? The local paper, specialty publications, bulletin boards, websites?
- Where do they hang out? The college gym, the park, the local rec center, the corner coffee shop?
- What are their other interests?

Questions Regarding the Publications in Which You May Choose to Advertise

- What is the publication's reputation and track record?
- Who is its target audience?
- How long has it been in existence?
- What is its circulation?
- What local businesses are advertising in it?
- How is the publication circulated?
- How much does it cost?

Questions Regarding the Website on Which You May Choose to Advertise

- How long has the site been in operation?
- How does the site build traffic?

- How do I track results?
- What reports do I receive?
- Am I getting unique inquiries?
- How many unique visitors does the site get (not just "hits")?

For small local businesses, outdoor (billboard and transit), TV, radio, and magazine advertising will likely not be cost-effective. However, don't discount small local access TV or radio stations. Just be sure to do your homework to ensure that their audience matches yours. If you decide to go with a print ad, make sure you read the fine print; is it a one-time ad, or are you locked into a long-term commitment with this publication? Ads may take six months or more to see a return on your investment, so be prepared to stay the course. It is likely your budget will be limited so when considering the purchase of advertising, it is best to look at all aspects of promotion before jumping to a decision.

iStockphoto/Thinkstock

#43: Advertising Legalities

Advertising can be a fun way to let your target market know you are the greatest trainer alive! Well, that may be overstating things, but you have to let people know you exist and are ready to help them achieve their goals. However, before you launch an advertising campaign, whether it's a complex campaign including newspaper ads and Internet promotion or something as simple as a flyer, it's important to ensure that what you claim in your advertising is accurate.

There are laws against deceptive advertising, so before launching any advertising, consider the following:

- Whatever you claim in your advertising, whether it's guaranteed results or weight loss, you have to be able to back that up. If you are selling nutritional supplements, don't make any assumptions or claims that are not medically proven by the manufacturer through scientific research.
- Steer clear of claiming that your product or service is "doctor" recommended, or recommended by anyone for that matter. You'll also want to steer clear of using photos or graphics of health-care professionals because that can imply that what you do is "recommended" by them.
- Implied celebrity endorsements, or using the image of celebrity, in your advertising is illegal. For example, using an image of Tom Venuto in your ad and stating that he loves your product or service when in fact he's never met you, let alone been trained by you, would set you up for a major lawsuit.
- If you advertise a money-back guarantee for a product or service, be specific in which circumstances the guarantee is offered. You can't make a general statement about a money-back guarantee and then write the rules when you're faced with an unhappy client.
- Pricing claims in ads must be accurate, especially if you choose to compare your price to that of a competitor. If you charge $75 per hour for personal training and your competitor's advertised price is $85, both prices must be legitimate (you won't change the price when they walk in the door) and sustainable (meaning you can actually make a living charging the lower price).

While advertising can be a key to attracting new customers and creating an image, be sure to think through the legal aspects to ensure that you accurately and truthfully represent your services or products.

#44: Sales Promotion

Another aspect of the promotional mix is sales promotion. The primary reasons companies use sales promotion are to increase demand, sales, and awareness for their product or service. You may be wondering how exactly sales promotion works and how you can incorporate it into your fitness business. There are many you've probably heard of and may have even used in the past.

- *Buy one, get one free*: A great concept to introduce products or services to clients, but be sure you determine how to break even and not lose money in a buy one, get one free offer.
- *Coupons*: These can be offered in several ways: online through a Web promotion where the customer prints them and brings them to your studio, in a newspaper print ad or supplemental insert, or even through a mobile phone. You'll want to anticipate your demand to ensure you have enough supply on hand or capacity.
- *Free samples*: If you offer products such as supplements or nutritional drinks, you can offer tastes or samples to your customers. You can even consider 15-minute mini-sessions to give the prospect a taste of what they will get from you in a personal-training session.
- *Cause-related*: By teaming up with a benefit race or raising money and awareness for a favorite cause, you will generate awareness and good will (for more information, see #71: For a Good Cause).
- *Competitions and prize drawings*: These are a great way to increase sales and gather demographic information on potential clients. You can offer competitions for existing clients or drawings for free services or products for new or potential customers.
- *Joint promotions with another vendor*: Teaming up with another business that offers something that complements what you do can be a win-win for both of you. For example, a fitness professional may team up with a natural supplement shop or massage therapist on special offers.
- *Rebates*: With rebates, your clients pay full price and mail in a certificate to receive a rebate. If you sell fitness products or supplements, you can always check with the manufacturer to see what special offers they may have for rebates.

Many types of sales promotion can positively influence the buying behavior of your current and potential customers. Sales promotion is an especially good tactic to stimulate demand in low-volume months, such as summertime. Put yourself in their shoes, and think about what may entice you to try a new product or service. Then, try it as part of your promotional mix.

#45: The Role of Newsletters

Newsletters are a great way to reach your customers on an ongoing basis at minimal cost to you. Sure, you see your regulars, but a consistent way to connect with those who you see a little less frequently is to create a brief, topical, and timely newsletter. A newsletter can be a cost-effective way to educate your customers on current topics, promote your business, create a positive image, and encourage them to use your services.

You already know what's of interest to them: fitness. That's why they come to you. In your overall promotional mix, consider the advantages of a newsletter. You may wonder that without a writing background, how and where do you start?

- First, be a student of your trade. Read current fitness publications and research. Become an expert in your field.
- Brainstorm with a friend or colleague to come up with topics for the year. Be sure you cover the hot fitness topics as well as tried-and-true research.
- Develop a monthly editorial calendar, with two-three relevant topics per month.
- Find some experts, perhaps at local universities, who may be willing to be quoted in your articles.
- Start writing!

Some simple rules to keep in mind when writing newsletter copy include:

- The introductory paragraph, or lead, should be catchy and let the reader know a little of what he will read.
- The body should develop in detail what is stated in the lead.
- The final paragraph should summarize what the reader has read.
- Always run a spell-check. You can lose credibility with misspelled words and typos.
- Ask someone to proofread your copy and provide feedback. An actual person can catch errors that spell-check applications miss—such as words that are spelled correctly but are used incorrectly.

Your newsletter also should include a reason to contact you, or a "call to action." It's an excellent opportunity to promote a monthly special or new product or service. That will most certainly help you to generate business. You can also include special offers such as "The first five readers who respond by e-mail to the special offer will receive a *free* personal-training session" or other sales promotion concepts like coupons to encourage your clients and prospects to read and respond to your newsletter.

A final consideration is how and where to distribute your newsletter. While you don't want to spend all your promotional dollars in one place, a newsletter can be inexpensive to distribute. You can e-mail it to your clients, post it on your website, make copies and give it to customers after a visit, or you can mail it.

#46: Cross-Promotion

Cross-promotion is a familiar concept, although you may not realize there is an actual term for it. There's the Coke can that doubles as a $4-off coupon for a local theme park, the grocery bag that promotes breast-cancer awareness every year, or the radio station that partners with a charitable organization on a fund-raising event.

These examples of cross-promotion involve the endorsement of a person, product, or a company by another in a way that benefits both (for more information, see Tip #71: For a Good Cause). A fan of the local water park will likely buy a Coke product to get the discount, and the regular Coke drinker may decide to try out the water park. A woman who's been affected by breast cancer who sees that a local grocer supports breast-cancer research may change her shopping habits to support that grocer. A loyal customer to the grocer may decide to start supporting breast-cancer research.

Cross-promotion can be a cost-effective way for businesses to promote themselves. If you team up with another business, you can connect with potential customers in places you might not have otherwise. If they were not previously your customers, they may develop an awareness of or even an appreciation of you as an individual. Cross-promotion can increase your client base.

You'll also benefit from the credibility you'll gain from association with a particular organization or product. In effect, you are endorsing them while they are endorsing you. If you team up with a well-respected, visible organization, you will be exposed to new potential customers. For example, partner with a massage therapist and for every 20 personal-training sessions purchased throw in a free massage. Work with the local supplement store and offer a free session for every $100 purchase of supplements. People like deals, no matter how large or small their checking account may be.

Advertising expenses also are shared by both organizations, so your costs are reduced. Consumers also are typically drawn to cross-promotions because they feature two different companies. The consumer will want to know why they are advertising together and may seek additional information.

If you decide to embark on cross-promotion, be sure to research the company or companies you want to approach. Consider your own goals, values, and needs as well as those of your customers and the company with which you want to partner. Remember that each party will have to benefit from the efforts, whether it's the woman who has decided to start shopping at the store that supports breast cancer research, the organization that will receive charitable dollars, or the personal trainer who gains new clients. Everyone needs to realize a win. Also make sure the company you choose to partner with has high ethical standards and shares similar wellness and business philosophies. This will prevent problems leading to negative public relations or a bad breakup between partners.

Finally, while you may want to start small the first time out by partnering with one other organization, don't limit yourself. Think about what you can accomplish by teaming up with several organizations, perhaps a health-food store and a charitable cause. The possibilities are nearly endless.

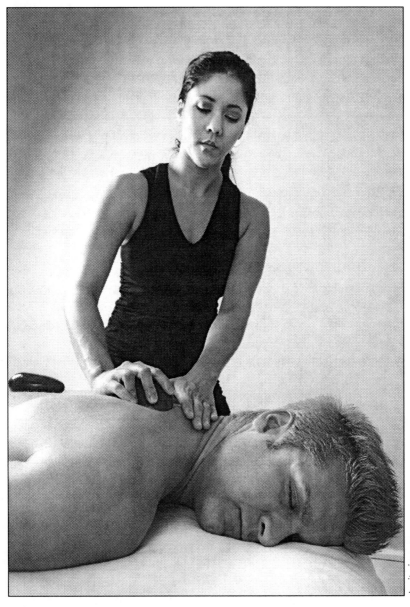

Jupiterimages

#47: Putting Public Relations to Work For You

The role of public relations (PR) is to enhance the image or perception of your business. Companies large and small desire a positive image because the attitude consumers have about your business can have a tremendous affect on sales. Large companies, such as Ben & Jerry's, can generate positive news stories through their socially responsible activities, while smaller businesses can do so through the support of local charities. Your goal is to help consumers understand and accept what you do—and create a positive image.

Public relations is typically a form of non-paid publicity that generates some media or discussion about your company. For example, say you're expanding your personal-training business and have hired a new trainer who will offer group "personal" training. Some public-relations activities that can be employed include the following:

- *Public speaking*: Addressing your local chamber of commerce or professional group
- *News releases*: A short written message sent to the local newspapers and radio stations to publicize an event or product or convey messages to the public (see the example in Table 47-1). You may want to contact the media by telephone first and find out how they prefer to receive it.
- *Blogs*: A type of website with commentary on a particular topic or events
- *Social media*: Such as Twitter, Facebook, and discussion boards

Regardless of the type of PR activity you use, remember that it's an opportunity to convey important messages about your values. What you say or write in a public forum will stick with people and help to build that positive image you desire. Also remember that PR is *free*. It is risky because there is no guarantee that a media outlet will pick up and run a news release, but if you link it to a hot topic in fitness, you can position yourself as the expert, increase awareness in your target market, and have a positive public perception of your business for zero dollars.

Exercise

Write a news release for something new you plan to offer your target market in the coming weeks. Be concise, but informative to convey your message.

Media Release

Contact:
Name and Title
Business Name
Telephone Number
E-mail Address

Date

For Immediate Release

Joe Smith Joins XYZ Fitness
New Group Personal Training Classes Forming

(Name of town, state) – XYZ Fitness announces the addition of Joe Smith, certified personal trainer and local fitness guru, to its staff of personal training experts. Smith, a graduate of ABC University, will launch a new group personal training format, which he perfected while training at the University of ABC ...

"The group personal training format complements our ...," says Name and Title, owner of XYZ Fitness.

[Use one of the following commonly accepted symbols to signify the end of the press release.]

-30-
or
###

Table 47-1. News release sample

#48: Identifying New Prospects

The exercise in #13: Who Is Your Market? helped you define your target market, or the segment of a population to whom you'll focus your marketing efforts. You found that you tend to train or want to target people with particular demographics or in a certain geographic area or with lifestyle traits that appeal to you. So now that you've identified who you want to target, the next step is how to find them and make them aware that you exist.

Attracting new prospects to build a strong business extends beyond handing out business cards. Everyone has business cards. To get prospects to hear what you have to offer, you will need to prove you are worthy of their time. Following are a few effective ways you can accomplish just that:

- *Develop a website*: Be sure to include information about what you do as a fitness professional, but also consider including health-related articles and links to other sites. Have an exercise or recipe of the month. Talk about your fitness philosophies and ideas.

- *Write and distribute a monthly newsletter*: There's almost no better way to let people know about your expertise and fitness philosophies. Don't let the thought of writing overwhelm you. As a fitness professional with a wide variety of knowledge about fitness, nutrition, and behavioral information, simply start by putting your thoughts to paper. E-mail your newsletter to your friends, family, and clients, and let it do your marketing for you. Soon you will have hundreds of potential leads each and every month. The best part is it will cost you virtually nothing but your time to research and write.

- *Consider posting articles, and starting a discussion board or blog on the Internet*: It's a great tool to get you noticed. Also, if you have a website, these are some great ways to drive more traffic to your site.

- *Set up an e-mail request section on your website*: Prospects surfing your website can ask you questions. It's an opportunity to start a conversation with a prospect and perhaps whet that person's appetite enough to convince him to hire you as his trainer.

- *Start presenting to different community groups*: Whether it is at your gym, a local business, chamber of commerce, or church, the more people you can stand in front of at one time, the better.

- *Look for free media*: Send out press releases to local newspapers. Call radio and television stations, and let them know you are the "local" expert about the latest, hottest trends in health and wellness. Never miss an opportunity to appear in print or on television or the radio.

Attracting prospects takes some innovative thinking and some work. Find what methods work for you, and hone your skills. The more you work at developing a consistent method to keep a steady flow of prospects, the easier it will become and the healthier your business will be.

Exercise

List three tools you can use to generate a steady flow of training prospects for your business.

1.
2.
3.

Set deadlines for when you will implement these tools into your marketing plan.

Hemera/Thinkstock

#49: Personal Selling

Personal selling is a way to inform and persuade customers or potential customers to purchase your products or services. As a personal trainer, personal selling may be the way you get your business launched or introduce new products or services to the community.

Large organizations typically will hire a sales staff. Most small businesses don't have that luxury, so your sales staff may just be you. With personal selling, you will want to talk with people who are potential customers, persuade them to buy your product or service, and keep them satisfied—and coming back.

Your potential clients will be seeking information about what you do and comparing you with other fitness providers. Therefore, you need to be confident and well-versed about what you do.

According to Pride and Ferrell (2008), personal selling involves seven steps:
- *Prospecting*: Developing a list of potential customers.
- *Pre-approach*: Doing your homework on the customers. For example if you are targeting female triathletes for fitness training, you'll want to find out where they typically train, what types of training programs or regimens they use, what fitness experts they listen to, and what fitness publications they read.
- *Approach*: How you contact the potential customer. This is your opportunity to get to know the person and gather information about their needs and objectives.
- *Making the presentation*: Getting the person's attention and generating interest. It's your opportunity to demonstrate what you offer and invite the prospect to try your product or service. You also must be a good listener and observe their response.
- *Overcoming objections*: Being prepared to address questions and provide solid information.
- *Closing*: Asking the person to buy your product or service. You may want to do this a few times throughout your presentation.
- *Following up*: Ensuring that the customer is satisfied. For example, if you employ several trainers and you've closed a deal with the human resources manager of a local company to offer wellness classes, you want stay in contact with that manager, as well as with the employees taking the classes.

Depending on how large or small your fitness business, you will likely engage in most of these personal selling steps. If you are prepared and take the time to listen to the needs of the potential client, you will be able to overcome objections and make the sale.

#50: Closing the Sale

Getting a potential client to say "Yes" can seem like a daunting task. It also can be as simple as asking the client for their business. If you've prepared adequately and taken the steps to present yourself and your fitness business in a positive light, you can do just that: ask them to be your client.

You can be the best fitness trainer in the business but unless you sell yourself—convince the potential client that you are the trainer for them—you won't be in business long. If you are prepared, closing the sale will become a natural part of your conversation with the client.

Regardless of what business you're in, there are some straightforward ways to help close the sale and get the client to say, "Yes, you are the fitness trainer for me." Listen carefully and ask questions so you can help your clients identify their needs. You are now prepared to show them how you will meet those needs.

- As you ask questions, listen for signs that they are ready to hire you as their trainer, such as, "What is your availability on Tuesdays?" or "What kind of specials can you offer me?"
- Be prepared to ask questions of your own. For example, the question about your availability on Tuesday could be answered with, "What times of the day work best for you?"
- Set a deadline to get a person to make a buying decision. If you're running a training special during the summer, encourage the potential client to get started before the offer ends, sending the message that you want them to get a deal.
- Set yourself apart by looking for ways to serve your customers better. Try to be a resource for the latest information, and be ready to help them do a better job.
- Consider offering choices by asking, "Which of these training packages do you prefer, A or B?"
- Show enthusiasm. This is such a simple yet overlooked trait when making a presentation. You don't have to possess in-your-face energy, but come on; this is about getting the client up and active. Show some zest in your presentation!

Regardless of how you try to close your sale, remember that the potential client should sense that you understand and care about helping them, not that you are just looking for a sale or a new client to add to your list. Nevertheless, if you don't ask for the sale, you may not get it. It is one of the hardest things to do in business, but it is crucial to you sealing the deal. Plus, it gets a lot easier once you get in the habit of doing it. Don't be shy. Ask to be their trainer.

#51: The World of Online Marketing

Everyone wants to be on the Internet and for good reason. The entrepreneurs who launched online companies such as Google™, Amazon, and eBay® have become very wealthy and their companies are household names.

While those are extreme, well-known examples, thousands of others have done well, expanding what they offer online and developing ways to create a need or desire for their products or services. Think about it this way: an entire generation of people grew up with a computer at home.

Internet marketing, or e-marketing, is a way to interact with current clients, share the benefits of your services or products with an entire new group of potential customers, and build a database of prospects. The Internet has opened up opportunities worldwide that previously did not exist through sharing information about products and services. For example, you can train clients living on other continents, sell supplements, or market an e-book. The sky is the limit.

Internet marketing can be a prime way to attract more people to your business, build customer relationships and enhance your branding. It also can create a sense of community among your customers. There are many Internet strategies to consider in your overall marketing mix, and while all Internet marketing strategies don't work for all businesses, it's a good idea to consider what is out there and determine how to incorporate it into your marketing strategy.

Having an Internet marketing strategy gives you a measurable and definitive way to target your market and position your business so that those looking for what you have to offer are finding you easily. There are many aspects to Internet marketing to consider, many of which are explored in upcoming chapters.

- Website
- Pay per click (you need a website)
- Search engine marketing
- Web display ads
- Blogs
- E-newsletters
- E-mail marketing
- Online freebies (craigslist)
- Viral marketing
- Posting on message boards
- Social media (Twitter, Facebook)

Check out InternetNews.com, a great resource for current thinking, statistics and articles on Web content, e-commerce, Internet advertising, and more. Then develop your own strategies to introduce your personal-training concepts to a whole new audience of potential customers.

#52: Launching a Website to Market Your Business

Every business seems to have a website. Retailers, manufacturers, and service companies alike have a story to tell, and what better and less expensive way to reach potentially millions of people than putting your business online? However, just because everyone has a website isn't a good enough reason to launch one yourself.

Before you decide that a website is right for your business, it's important to establish why you really want one and what you hope to accomplish with it. You may want to ask yourself the following questions:

- Who is your target audience?
- How do they prefer to receive information?
- Do you have several services or products to sell that can be illustrated online?
- Will your content change frequently?
- If so, who will be in charge of updating it?
- Is there some sort of action you hope clients or potential clients will take based on the information you provide on your website?

Once you've determined that a website is the way to go, you have a couple options for getting it built:

- Hire a professional Web designer, who will be able to consider your overall marketing goals and design a site that reflects your fitness philosophies. A designer also is knowledgeable about how to build logical navigation into the site. They also will recommend a website host.
- Create your own website. Web-hosting sites such as web.com and http://smallbusiness.yahoo.com/webhosting provide templates you can easily follow to create a website. While these are more cost-effective than hiring a professional, they will limit your ability to customize your site to reflect your brand.

You also will need to select a domain name. A domain name is the .com, .net, .info name, which is used to identify your website. It's important to choose a good domain name for your website. Go to a search engine, and type in "domain registration," and see how many results come up. GoDaddy.com is an Internet domain registrar and web-hosting company, and you can purchase a domain name for a very minimal investment.

Finally, be sure to promote your website. Include the URL on your business cards and in all your marketing materials. Tell your clients about the site and its features. With hundreds of thousands of websites in today's market, you should not expect people to just know you have a site. Drive people to your site via e-newsletters, postings on message boards, blogging, and such.

Your website should become an integral component of your marketing strategy. You've spent the money to create it, now let it do some marketing for you because it can do something you physically cannot: work 24 hours a day, seven days a week.

iStockphoto/Thinkstock

#53: Making Your Website Valuable

Establishing a website is an inexpensive way to open your business to more customers, improve your professional image, and promote your goods and services to an expanded market. Websites also help you keep customers coming back by allowing them to easily visit your site, see what you are doing, and watch for specials, features, sales, and information

If you build, it doesn't necessarily guarantee that they will come. The primary purpose of your website should be getting the visitor to return. The words and images on your site are powerful marketing tools and will turn visitors into customers. The wrong words and images may send them to another site, never to return to yours. Consider the following when developing your content:

- *Write to persuade*. Write as if you are having a conversation with person. Identify a problem, and validate the visitor's need for a solution. Explain why your product is the solution. Pack your copy with benefits and more benefits.

- *Increase awareness of your services or products*. Feature every service or product you offer. You may have customers who aren't aware of some other features of your business. If you sell products, a website means you are open 24 hours a day, seven days a week.

- *Integrate your Web efforts with your traditional marketing*. Your website enhances and leverages your other marketing efforts. Websites also are quicker, easier, and more cost-effective to update than print-based media.

- *Build on your branding*. If you've created a brand, your site can reinforce it, having the same look and feel as any of your marketing materials, business card, and advertising. Additionally, those aspects should feature your URL prominently.

#54: Display Ads

Online display ads are everywhere, and they get more creative—in some cases, even more annoying—all the time. Go to your favorite news site, health site, or retail portal, and you'll see ads bordering the Web pages containing logos, flashy words, photos, and even video clips.

Online display ads (or banner ads) are here to stay and can be a way to target your specific customers. Your ad can be as simple as a logo or icon along the margin of the page or a sophisticated ad that opens across the page.

An advantage of display ads is that they provide features that other forms of advertising cannot. Your ad can link directly to your website. It can change daily, depending on what products or services you have to offer or what specials consumers are responding to. Online display ads can provide instant feedback.

The prices of ads will vary, depending on the site and number of visitors. Typically, display ads are priced based on how many people visit the website. Say, for instance, you have an ad on the local newspaper website. The salesperson will tell you how many people visit the site daily. Great, right? Thousands of visitors a day may add up to many new customers.

Another idea would be to negotiate placing a banner ad on the website of a business that is a complementary service to personal training, such as massage therapy, wedding planners (brides looking to get in shape), spas, and salons. It may be possible to trade banner ads with that business resulting in little to no financial investment on your part.

Do your homework. Be sure that the consumers you are targeting are frequent users of the website on which you want to advertise. Ask the site owner for statistics on the types of people who use the site—how many are new visitors and how many site visits are repeat. Be choosy about where you advertise, and regardless of the site or sites you select, be sure that your ads reflect the values of your business. If you're considering advertising on a website that has values that conflict with yours, you may want to rethink your strategy and look elsewhere.

#55: Pay Per Click

Pay per click is an online advertising method used on search engines, such as Yahoo! and Google, and on blogs, in which the advertiser pays the host site only when a reader clicks on the sponsored link. Typically, companies wanting to advertise will bid on a word or phrase relevant to their line of business for the right to have prominent placement on the search engine page.

Because you're specifying certain words or phrases, the person searching the word already has an interest in what you do. People can simply click your ad to link to your website, make a purchase, or learn more about you.

For example, enter the term "fitness books" in Google. The "Sponsored Links" you find at the top of the page and along the right-hand margin are examples of companies that are paying a certain fee each time someone clicks on their link. The link takes you directly to the advertiser's website.

An advantage of pay-per-click advertising is that you can advertise locally or regionally. If your business is in Orlando, you can advertise within a certain mile radius of your location. And you are in control of the cost. You may choose to spend $5 per day to have your ad on the display. If the cost is 10 cents each time a potential customer clicks your link, your ad will remain visible until the 50th person clicks your ad. Most sites also will provide reports to you on how well your ad is performing.

Pay-per-click advertising can be an effective part of your Internet marketing mix. Be sure to explore several search engines and blog to see what words and phrases are popular and try it out. Again, you can control the cost and it can be an inexpensive addition to your advertising.

#56: Search Engine Optimization

Search the Internet on any particular topic using any of the popular search engines and you'll see that some sites come up consistently. Search most or any medical or health issues and WebMD or Mayo Clinic are among the top sites listed.

In a nutshell, these sites have great content and have been submitted to search engines. A site with good content will be indexed and the search engines will be able to find your content easily. How does it happen? A basic primer on how search engines work will be helpful.

Search engines do not search the entire Internet for content. The search engines search their own indexes of information. The way they get the information into their databases is through programs called spiders or robots that search the Internet, take notes, report back to the search engine, and store the information in a database.

You'll first need to submit your website to the search engines. You'll generally do this as soon as you launch your site. By submitting your site to the search engines, you are inviting their robots to index your site. It will make your site and its content highly relevant for both search engines and searchers.

The following are some search engines to which you'll want to submit your website:
• Google
• Yahoo!
• MSN Live Search
• Ask.com

Then you'll need to have good content on your site. If you build it, they won't necessarily come. Submitting your site to search engines, coupled with meaningful content and frequent updates, will help consumers find your site and lead to potential new business.

#57: E-mail Marketing

E-mail marketing has grown exponentially in recent years, influencing buying behavior and decision making. It can have a tremendous impact on your personal training business. Think about the e-mails that hit your inbox daily—those that you've opted to receive. It's likely that you've either taken action on at least one of those, whether making a purchase or even telling others about the content of what you've read. E-mail is an inexpensive way for businesses to promote their goods and services to their current and prospective customers.

Consumers sign up to receive e-mails to notify them of things of interest to them. Those retailers or other sources hope to influence consumer behavior with news from a favorite magazine or newspaper, sales at favorite retailers, newsletters on topics of interest such as health and wellness, or alumni information from their alma mater.

The retailer or organization then contacts the subscriber on a regular basis because they have developed a relationship, even if it's a single purchase. It becomes an opportunity for that retailer or business to build on an existing relationship and create a bond that will keep the customer coming back. For example, if you have an e-newsletter, make sure you attempt to get every customer or prospect on your mailing list.

There are two groups—existing customers and potential customers—you can target with e-mail. Each will likely have different needs because with your current customer group, you already have relationship.

The easiest way to get started is to gather e-mail addresses from your current clients. You can simply ask for their e-mail address so you can send them information about products or services, or you can run a promotion or contest and ask for an e-mail address on the contest form.

Some reasons you may decide to e-mail clients include:
- A promotion on training, such as buy 10 sessions, get the 11th session free
- Refer a friend, and receive a discount or freebie

E-mail Tips

- Everyone's inboxes are cluttered. Think about your message and your subject line. According to MailerMailer's Email Marketing Metrics Report from Fall 2007, subject lines with fewer than 35 characters get the best response rates.
- Be sure that what you're advertising or promoting fits in with any other advertising you are doing. You want them to complement one another and support your overall marketing campaign and messages.

- Ask people to pass along your message to others who may have interest in what you are doing. For example, ask them to forward your e-newsletter to create viral marketing.
- Give people the option to "unsubscribe" to your e-mail.
- Make your subject lines brief and brilliant.

When sending your clients e-mail, think about all the e-mail messages you receive daily, what annoys you, and what inspires you. Placing yourself in your clients' shoes will help to ensure that your e-mails are worthy of opening.

iStockphoto/Thinkstock

#58: To Blog or Not to Blog—That Is the Question

These days, blogs are becoming a more respected and important method of communications. A blog (short for Web log) is an online publication of a person's thoughts and ideas to which readers may choose to respond. The blog is the opinion of the blogger, and typically, the blogger develops an audience who is interested in the particular topics being posted.

Successful bloggers are specific and passionate about their topics, posting information on a regular basis. The readers of the blog play a significant role in the popularity and success of a blog. Those comments give the blogger feedback on postings, what's working and what's not, and can serve as inspiration for subsequent posts. The people who keep coming back will feel a sense of ownership with the blog and will defend the blogger's position, in many cases.

Whether you're a frequent reader of blogs, have never read one, or already have your own, a blog can be an effective marketing tool to reach current and prospective clients. Developing a following of readers will take time, but if you have the desire to dedicate some of your time to blogging, you have another opportunity to establish yourself as an expert or authority on a topic for which you are passionate. This is also a great forum to share your philosophies on health and fitness, get up on a soapbox to rant on a controversial subject, or simply pay it forward by sharing bits of your knowledge to the world. You never know when something you blog may click with a reader, ultimately changing that person's life!

Before you decide whether to launch a blog and start sharing your thoughts with the world, search existing blogs on fitness to see what's out there and develop ideas. Then, visit blog-hosting sites such as blogspot.com, blogger.com, blogit.com, and thoughts.com to get started.

#59: Viral Marketing

When you visit a store or restaurant and receive superior service, you likely tell a friend or two about your experience. You, too, have been around friends and family members excited to tell you about the latest movies they saw, products they tried, and services they enjoyed.

Simply put, you are participating in viral marketing, a concept that encourages customers to pass along marketing messages about a business and its products or services—those positive messages they want others to know. Typically, satisfied customers will tell an average of 8 to 10 friends and family members about a good experience You obviously want your clients to do the same for you.

Viral marketing can be intentional, such as hiring temporary staff to talk about your services where you train and with friends in casual situations. However, unless they actually train with you, their sales pitch or testimonial may not seem genuine.

An even better way to initiate viral marketing is through your existing clientele. Your best customers can be your best marketers. You've probably already gotten referrals from your clients. Why not step up the ante and ask them to talk about your training services with their friends? You can offer incentives, discounts, or gift cards as "payment" for their marketing efforts. You can even go so far as training someone free of charge, and in return, require that person to talk about your training.

A great example of viral marketing is the success of Heather Koelling of Webster Groves, Missouri. One class she offers is a boot camp from her home on Monday mornings. She's never advertised it, but started out with a small group of friends. Eventually, those friends told their friends, and before long, Heather had a steady stream of women enrolled in her boot camps.

With viral marketing, you're business can begin marketing itself, and before you know it, new business will start rolling in.

#60: Is YouTube for You?

YouTube is an Internet sensation. It's the third-most popular site in the world, after Google and Yahoo! People love watching online videos. Businesses of all types are using YouTube and other video sites to reach current and potential customers with messages about their produces and services. It can be a cost-effective advertising method you should consider as part of your marketing mix.

Video marketing is fairly easy and inexpensive. It's not hard to create a short video and get it posted. While your fitness business can benefit from a presence on YouTube and other video sites, getting people to watch your videos may be tricky. Be sure that your video shows various aspects of your business and mentions your business name.

If you decide to embark on advertising through YouTube, it's important to consider the following:

- Create a business account on YouTube, especially if you already have a personal account. The only videos you want posted on your fitness YouTube account are your videos demonstrating fitness techniques and products.
- Put thought into the title of your video. It should be interesting, descriptive, and brief. You'll also want to make sure that your title and description has keywords that search engines will pick up.
- Make the video brief. It should be no shorter than 30 seconds and no longer than a couple minutes. Consumers won't want to watch a long video.
- Think about what makes you tune into a video on YouTube. Popular YouTube videos tend to be funny, controversial, or contain pertinent information.
- To convey a professional image, use good video equipment including lighting and cameras. Viewers will take you more seriously.
- Post your video on other video sites like Vimeo and AdWido™ to maximize the potential exposure you can get for just one video.
- Post your videos on your website, too. At least initially, you're going to get more traffic on your videos from your own site.

To get your name out there on YouTube, after you've posted your video or videos, search on similar fitness content and comment on and rate those videos. Comment and rate videos as often as possible, because others viewing those videos may try to contact you or will want view your videos. Make your comments brief but meaningful, because they are permanent.

Finally, because it's inexpensive, try it out and have fun with it. If you produce some short, decent videos, it's just another way of adding value for your customers who visit your website. Even if it isn't Hollywood, your clients will be impressed they are training with an Internet sensation. Milk it for all it is worth. You are the product.

#61: Posting on Message Boards

A message board is simply an online discussion that takes place on a particular topic. The forum or message board host site typically has rules and polices that govern content. Many types of businesses start message boards to market themselves and to control and monitor what's being said about them. Other message boards are started because someone wants to launch a discussion on a topic of interest.

Posting on message boards is another way to get your name in the public eye, establish yourself as a local fitness expert, and generate interest in your fitness business.

Readers who are interested in fitness topics and have fitness questions may log onto sites such as healthboards.com, diet.ivillage.com/messageboards, or www.freetrainers.com/FT/jsp/MessageBoards.jsp seeking answers or discussion. Check out these sites for some ideas on types of questions and discussions that are going on. To promote your fitness services, however, you will want to focus locally when posting on message boards.

Do an online search of "fitness message boards" and the name of your city to see what types of message boards are popular in your area. Then, do the research to find out the rules and policies of the site. Local readers interested in fitness will be the ones reading, posting, and asking questions. Becoming the expert who answers their questions online and provides training advice may very well turn into some new business for you. You are developing trust, building relationships, and establishing yourself as an expert—and all it will cost you is your time.

Jupiterimages

#62: Becoming the Local Fitness Expert— How to Get Noticed

Most cities or towns, depending on the size, have a local fitness pro or two that the media go to time and time again for their comments and expertise for health-related stories. Somehow, that person has become the fitness expert. Whether it's the trainer's education, ingenuity, luck, or a combination of these factors, the traits that will take you the furthest are consistency and good old-fashioned hard work.

Remember the importance of building your brand. That style, look, or persona needs to consistent each and every time. When you hear the name Richard Simmons, you think big hair, tank tops, short-shorts, and off-the-wall energy. Who knows how he dresses and acts on his own time, but when he makes appearances, he always dresses the part. He is being his brand.

Next, get out there and let people know about your brand. Try some of the following activities, and make contact with people who can help you build your credibility as an expert:

- *Meet with physicians*. Pharmaceutical reps call on physicians to push their products, and you can do the same. Put together a short, polished presentation, and then be prepared to sit in the waiting room. Get testimonials from clients along with solid stats that show you can make a difference in their patient's health. When meeting with physicians, make it quick. Two minutes may be all the time you'll get.
- *Pay attention to the hot trends in health and wellness*. When a new research finding, study, or newsworthy story about fitness hits the airwaves, contact the stations or newspapers to let them know you can serve as an expert on the subject.
- *Do something charitable*. Volunteer to lead running groups to train people for events like the Susan G. Komen Race for the Cure®, and then send out press releases to all the local media. Public relations (for more information, see #47: Putting Public Relations to Work for You) is virtually free, and if a station bites, you can link your business with solid cause-related marketing.
- *Write articles for a local newspaper*. A paid column would be a great gig, but if you are unknown, it may take a lot to convince an editor you are worth the money. Regardless, your stories will be delivered to hundreds or thousands of homes, and you will begin to build one of the most important components of becoming the local expert: credibility.

Of course, it always helps to know someone. Networking will play a huge role in your quest to become the go-to trainer by local media, but everyone has to start somewhere. Think big, look for opportunity, and keep scratching your way up. One more piece of advice: Unless you are in the back of a police car, never pass up the chance to be on television, in the newspaper, or on the radio. These opportunities must be seized.

#63: E-Books

You can't be in two places at once. As a trainer, unless you add group training or boot camps to your product line, you can only see so many clients in a day. Ideally, you can make money without seeing clients. It's not as far fetched as it sounds if you capitalize on opportunities available on the Internet.

Consumers spend millions of dollars each year on health and fitness DVDs, books, and magazines, including online informational products such as e-books. While writing isn't something everyone wants or even can do, fitness professionals can get a piece of that action by writing an e-book and creating something of value that requires no inventory. An e-book can turn your website from informational to revenue generating, making money while you sleep.

To get started, first you'll need a topic. It needs to be comprehensive, yet not too broad. Tackling something like weight loss will have you writing the second coming of *War and Peace*. Start with what you know. Put pen to paper, and turn your Monday-morning boot camp into an electronic version of the workout that can be sold to current clients or to random surfers who come to your site.

Some things to consider if you pursue writing an e-book include:
- Talk with your Webmaster on how to set up a PayPal™ button and a system to automatically send a copy of the e-book once a payment is made.
- Consult a lawyer to help construct a legal disclaimer and to make sure you protect your intellectual property.
- Shop around to see what your competitors are charging for informational products and e-books.
- Find someone to help edit and proofread your materials.

You can add "author" to your list of credentials and create an additional revenue stream in the process.

#64: Social Media

Human beings have a need for social interaction. They like to be with other people most of their waking hours. It seems that as more families have become dual-income families, they are finding less time to spend on social activities while their need for social interaction has remained steady.

As a result, face-to-face interactions have decreased, and online interactions have increased. Social media has taken hold in mainstream America. Everywhere you turn, people are on their iPhones and PDAs accessing Facebook, Twitter, YouTube, Linked In, and more to keep in touch.

As a personal trainer, you want to know how to effectively use social media and add it to your marketing mix of tools to reach clients and potential clients with the marketing messages you want to convey. You want to be sure that what you develop in the social-media arena works hand-in-hand with your more traditional marketing tools.

First, you'll need to realize that your social-media marketing strategy will differ from a traditional marketing strategy in that you want to engage your audience in a conversation, not just send them your marketing messages. Social media depends on interactions to build relationships. You're using the Internet to interact versus being face-to-face or conveying your messages in a typical marketing medium such as print.

Then, explore the social media outlets that exist. Log on to Twitter, establish an account, and search words related to fitness to see how other fitness professionals may be using it. Establish a professional profile on LinkedIn.com so others can see your resume and interests. Search fitness blogs to see what others are doing.

You also can choose to join existing groups online to discuss topics and leave comments on blogs or message boards. The audience will choose to participate in your social media forum by adding comments, graphics, or video. Regardless of the forum or forums you choose, they will help you build an online presence and get people to notice what you're about.

So what is the take-home message with social media and your personal training business? It is about establishing or maybe reestablishing relationships—the same thing that has been discussed over and over again throughout this book! Sites like Facebook allow you to reconnect with long-lost friends, schoolmates, and college pals all wanting to know what you are up to these days. It almost seems too easy, and is a lot of fun in the process. Again, the point isn't to hammer every Facebook update or tweet with something health and fitness related; people will see through that in a millisecond. The point is to use these online sources to continue building relationships and over time subtly plug your business. Something like: "So, what are you up to these days? I live in Denver with my wife and two kids. She stays at home, and I run my own personal-training business. You said you recently ran a half-marathon? That is awesome! I did as well. Would you like to get on my e-newsletter list? There are a lot of fitness and nutrition tips that will help your training!"

It all starts with a little research, a willingness to try something new, and the desire to reach out to potential clients, and possibly old friends, in different ways—ways that are becoming more and more common the busier we become. Have fun with it, and see where it takes you.

Stockbyte

#65: How to Find Yourself on Yahoo!

Search your name on any search engine, and see what comes up. Now search the names of some of your competitors. You hope that your name appears in search engines more often or listed higher than the trainer down the road. If not, you can do some specific things to ensure that your name comes up higher in the search.

- *Purchase pay-per-click ads and listings on the Internet* (see more in #55: Pay Per Click). You can also get a lot of free hits just by doing what we have talked about over and over in this book. Get out, and be visible.
- *Get media exposure.* The Internet is like a giant sponge, so the more your name appears in newspapers, on television, and on the radio as the local fitness expert, the greater the likelihood you will get more hits on the Internet. If you do a piece for the local television station, the station will run the same story on their website. Same for radio. Newspapers share stories with sister newspapers, so while you may serve as the expert for a newspaper in Chicago, don't be surprised to see that same article appear in a newspaper in Houston.
- *Have your Webmaster hide bits of code, called meta tags, which will help classify your website into relevant groups.* If a person searches for a specific group such as "personal trainers" in a certain city, there is a better chance your site will be one of the hits that appear. Your Webmaster can help word language on your website so Internet searches will latch on to these keywords or phrases and place you higher on the results list.
- *Create a links page with other trainers or reciprocal businesses.* The more links you have, the higher you will rank on search engines.
- *Continue to practice becoming the local expert.* Post videos to YouTube, write articles for newspapers or online journals, and post on message boards. Write, and write often. Submit as much fresh material as you can.

The more positive stories, events, and activities you can link yourself to and get posted, the more hits you'll get and the higher your name will come up in the search engines. Google your name a few months after trying some of these suggestions, and see what happens.

5

Placement—How and Where Your Product Will Be Distributed

Brand X Pictures

#66: Expand Your Business by Marketing to Businesses

One of the most basic principles of business is that to stay in business, you must make a profit. Sometimes, making a profit means expanding your market beyond your current customer base and marketing to other businesses.

The concept of business-to-business marketing is simple. Businesses of all kinds rely on other businesses to fulfill the needs for products and services, whether for resale, to produce other products, to help the business operate, or for consumption by employees.

As a fitness professional, you can offer businesses a great deal. Consider that in 2007, the annual premium that a health insurer charged an employer for a health plan covering a family of four averaged $12,100. According to the National Coalition on Health Care, as of 2008 health-insurance expenses were the fastest-growing cost component for employers. The best way to control health-care costs is to prevent illness, disease, and disability before it happens. While some employers resist spending on wellness, others embrace the concept.

To get started, your first step is to pick up the phone and find out what local companies are doing or need in wellness programming. Determine whether they have a budget for wellness, if they have an onsite fitness facility, and what kinds of wellness programs (such as smoking cessation or weight loss) the employees want to see offered. It helps if you already have a contact in the prospective business, but if you don't, set up a sales call with the human resources manager.

Once you understand the company's vision for wellness, you can develop a cost-effective wellness strategy. For example, Integrated Wellness Concepts, LLC developed a team-based weight-loss program for Zeller Electric in 2007. The eight-week program consisted of online exercise and nutrition consulting, four 30-minute education sessions, and four team weigh-ins. By the end of the eight weeks, teams were using their lunch breaks to walk, and the entire business experienced a change in attitude about health and wellness.

Brainstorm some wellness programming ideas of your own, take your ideas to a business, and let them choose from your menu of options. Prove that you can improve the company's bottom line, and you will have a completely different segment in which to market your services. As you improve their bottom line, your profits will soar.

Exercise

Brainstorm a list of services you can bundle together and market to local businesses.

1.
2.
3.
4.
5.
6.
7.
8.
9.
10.

Jupiterimages

#67: Subcontracting to Generate New Business

The first thing that may come to mind when you hear the word subcontracting is construction. It's common practice for building contractors to hire specialists to complete specific tasks or areas of work, such as plumbing or electrical, for them.

Subcontracting, by definition, is hiring—or contracting with—someone to do a portion of some work you've been hired to do. In the construction example, the general contractor may hire a plumber as a subcontractor; however, the fulfillment of the work is the responsibility of the original contracting party: the general contractor.

According to the U.S. Small Business Administration, a subcontract is a contract between a prime contractor and a subcontractor to furnish supplies or services for the performance of a prime contract or subcontract.

A personal trainer can find value, and even new business, by subcontracting in a couple ways: as the general contractor or as the "plumber."

As a "general contractor," you have clients for whom you provide certain personal-training services. You train them on the proper techniques, guiding them to help them reach their goals. By hiring a subcontractor, such as a dietitian, you can expand your client base by offering comprehensive weight-loss services that include your one-on-one training along with the nutrition counseling and diet planning provided by the dietitian.

As a "plumber," you can provide services for another business or contractor to help supplement their product or service lines and expand their businesses as well as your own. You may work for a chiropractor to help train patients in preventive measures to reduce pain. You can provide personal-training services at the local YMCA or rec center. You may work during the football season at the high school as a trainer for the athletes.

The general contractor's greatest concern will be whether the subcontractors finish the work for which they've been hired and provide high-quality services. From the subcontractor's perspective, it's whether the contractor will follow through with what they've promised and pay them in a timely manner.

Regardless of the concerns, subcontracting is a great way to expand your business, find new clients, and generate more revenue for your own business. Do your homework before contracting with another business or individual and work with people you know and trust.

#68: Penetrating the Business Market

In an up-and-down economy, fitness and wellness programs are often the first to go when times get tough, despite the fact that when properly implemented, they save money and improve productivity. They can also be incredibly lucrative, which is why you should consider including business markets in your personal-training business.

Most likely, you will begin the task to penetrate business markets much like the high-powered executives who run them: at the bottom. But you have to start somewhere.

First, figure out what you have to offer the company, whether it's wellness coaching, coordinating a weight-loss incentive plan, starting an on-site boot camp, or consulting on the development of an employee fitness room. The more talents you bring to the table, the more valuable you are to the prospective client. Before you do your first sales call, research the company, anticipate needs, and develop the menu of products you plan to present.

Second, you need a name. Not your name, but the name of someone in the company who's a champion for employee wellness. This is easier said than done because you're not going to make a sales presentation without an appointment. This is where networking comes into the equation. Start with a company where a friend works, and ask them provide you with the commodity you most desire: names.

Finally, determine who the gatekeeper is. Pharmaceutical representatives have mastered this technique. They know who in the office can get them in to see the physicians. Your goal should be the same: figure out who can get you in touch with the people in power. Win them over, and you are one step closer to sealing the deal.

Never underestimate the power of a business market. It can mean the difference between one client at a time or a company filled with hundreds of clients. Which would you prefer?

#69: Getting Past the Gatekeeper

Once you have developed a list of businesses you plan to target, the next step is securing an opportunity to make a sales presentation to the decision maker in those specific businesses—which means you have to get past the gatekeeper.

Most businesses have a lengthy purchase approval process. Typically, the person who makes the final decision is further up the food chain and more difficult to contact than employees at lower levels such as secretaries and technical personnel. These individuals tend to be the gatekeepers or the people who control the flow of information to and from the people who make the decisions. You need to determine who has the decision-making power, but you will have to get through that initial level of defense the gatekeeper provides.

The pharmaceutical industry has mastered this skill because to get past the waiting-room door to make a call on a physician, they first have to develop a relationship with the secretary at the front desk. They also develop relationships with the nursing staff and other employees in the office. Why? Because it is easier to get a doctor to say "Yes" to your brand of prescription drug if you have a relationship with the office staff and they like you.

The following tips below will help you get through the gatekeeper to the person who will say "Yes" to your product or service:

- *Research*. Know who you want to talk with before calling. Use the Internet, library, or mutual acquaintances to find out who the decision-maker is. Learn their names and how to pronounce their names so that when you call you will sound like an acquaintance instead of a sales call.
- *Get to know the gatekeeper*. You want the gatekeeper working for you, not against you. Develop that relationship. Once you solidify that relationship, that person will be more likely to open the door to the people you really need to talk with: the decision-makers.
- *Be creative*. Send your marketing materials along with something that will demonstrate how your services will improve the health of their employees. A flyer or, if you have the means, a promotional DVD (such as 10 Ways to Work Out While at Work) will give a company a taste of what you do.
- *Know when to call*. Decision-makers usually arrive early and leave late. If you haven't yet developed a relationship with the gatekeeper, calling at these times increases your odds of connecting directly with the decision-maker.
- *Find common ground*. Try to find out if you share anything in common with the decision-maker. The easiest way to develop a relationship is to find common ground.

- *Be brief on voice mail.* If you get the gatekeeper's voice mail, briefly introduce yourself, and mention a mutual referral or relationship as the connecting point. Leave your number, e-mail address, and a time you'll call back.
- *Ask for referrals.* An easy way to get a new customer is by asking for referrals from your current customer base. Do your job right, and customers will be more than happy to refer you to a colleague.

Creatas Images

#70: Fitting the Product to the Client

To understand what it means to fit your product or service to the needs of your clients, take a look at the historical perspective of marketing. The three distinct eras in marketing show the evolution of how businesses developed product and services for their customers.

In the production era, there was a high demand for manufactured goods. The sales era reflected a time when demand for these products began to decrease and companies realized they had to "sell" their products to buyers—a sales-oriented philosophy. During the marketing era, companies realized they had to first listen and then respond to the customer's needs (Pride and Ferrell, 2008).

The marketing era ushered in the marketing concept, rooted in the belief that a company should focus on customers' needs and wants and develop products or services that satisfy these needs (Churchill and Peter, 1998). As personal trainers, your business is about developing exercise and nutrition plans to improve a client's health, fitness, and well-being. However, if you miss the point of the marketing concept, you risk running your business with a sales-oriented philosophy.

The next time you talk with a prospect, spend the better part of your time listening. You may have a great services and nutritional products available for purchase, but you may discover that's not what the client wants. Although you are the fitness expert, understanding why a client or prospect is sitting in front of you has a tremendous amount of worth. You may know what the client needs, but that isn't always what the client wants. Tailor the plan of action for what the client requests. You can always add more as the client becomes more confident in their progress. Resist the urge to cram your product line down their throats. It isn't about you; it is about the needs of the client.

Listen to the concerns, experiences, and failures of clients and prospects. Find out what they like about exercise or perhaps what they hate. Ask probing questions to get them talking, and then shut up and listen. They will tell you what they are looking for, which will make your job a lot easier.

Once you understand what the client needs, you can match your service or product to satisfy those specific needs. The marketing concept allows you, as the business owner, to adjust your product line to meet and satisfy the needs of your customers. By doing so, you will gain loyalty, beat competitors, and even develop a referral source for new business for life.

#71: For a Good Cause

Cause-related marketing is somewhat similar to community relations in that your actions are promoting your business. However, two organizations reap the benefits: yours and a non-profit of your choice.

The Foundation Center (www.foundationcenter.org) defines cause-related marketing as the public association of a for-profit company with a nonprofit organization, intended to promote the company's product or service and to raise money for the nonprofit.

Simply put, it is linking your business to a particular social cause. It usually involves some sort of a cooperative undertaking by your for-profit business with a non-profit organization for a mutual benefit. According to Pride and Ferrell (2006), the term "cause-related marketing" can be attributed to American Express, which in 1983, made a donation to the restoration of the Statue of Liberty every time customers used their American Express cards. Cause marketing has grown tremendously in the past 25 years, and for good reason. Since American Express introduced the concept, thousands of non-profit organizations have reaped the benefits of the for-profit world's consumer loyalty and association with a cause.

For you, as a business owner, it can increase sales and create feelings of good will or admiration about you and your company among current customers as well as potential customers. Among the possible benefits of cause marketing for businesses include positive public relations, improved customer relations, and additional marketing opportunities. Think about how you can highlight your reputation within your target market. Cause-related marketing can positively differentiate you from your competitors and provide an edge that delivers other tangible benefits, including:

• Increased sales
• Increased visibility
• Increased customer loyalty
• Enhanced company image

During National Breast Cancer Awareness Month (October), you may consider donating a certain amount of dollars of every personal training session to Susan G. Komen for the Cure, or perhaps a local hospital could benefit from your donations. Brainstorm with friends or family members. Do you have a family member or friend who has a medical condition, such as heart disease? Is the local library planning an addition? The possibilities are endless. Pick something you feel strongly about, and you're sure to be motivated. Once you've nailed down your cause, contact the organization and let them know what you'd like to do. The organization, large or small, may even be able to help you promote whatever it is you choose to do to raise money for them.

Some examples and case studies—including the benefits and lessons learned in cause-related marketing—can be found at http://www.independentsector.org/ mission_market/policies.htm. The site also features a section—Cause Marketing Guidelines from the American Cancer Society—that you may find helpful.

Hemera/Thinkstock

#72: Partnering Up

Another great way to increase your business and find new clients is by partnering with another trainer who shares your interests and values. Partnering with someone enables you to branch out and reach new clients and potentially increase your income. With a general partnership, your business is owned by two or more people, not just yourself.

Partnering takes the concepts of networking a step further because you are working together to package your services and offer them to potential clients. You also are combining your talents to generate new income. For example, perhaps one of you is more comfortable talking with new or potential clients to bring in new business, while the other is great at upselling services to long-term customers. Your reputation within the local business community for on-site employee wellness can be enhanced by a partner with skills that will add more value to the employer.

Partners also can cover each other's responsibilities and generate income when the other is not available to train. Everyone gets sick at least once in a while, and you certainly deserve an occasional vacation. A partnership allows you to fill in on training sessions for each other.

From a business perspective, the partners share equally in the profits of the business and are liable for the expenses and debts, such as advertising dollars, equipment costs, and start-up costs, if any. Your partner needs to be someone you know and trust, so pick your partner carefully. You'll want to know as much as you can about the potential partner. Once you decide that a partnership is the way to go, you'll want to have an attorney draw up a contract that outlines each partner's responsibilities.

As you can see, advantages to a partnership can extend beyond what you can do on your own. Just remember to pick your partner carefully, and don't enter into a partnership lightly. Batman and Robin were the dynamic duo. Partner up, become the local fitness superheroes of your market, and dominate your competition.

6

It's All About the Relationships

Barry Austin

#73: Forging Relationships That Matter

Managing your customers sounds easy, right? Just make sure you stay in touch, and provide great exercise sessions. What else do you need to do? Your customers are loyal to you, and that's all you need to know. But if you're not careful, your most loyal customer may be shopping the competition if you're not delivering exactly what they've come to expect: programs and services tailored to their specific wants and needs.

Everyone knows that it costs less to maintain current customers than to attract new ones. A little extra time spent on managing those relationships can pay bigger dividends in the long run. That's where a little extra time and effort toward customer relationship management (CRM) can pay big dividends. The website destinationCRM.com defines CRM as "a company-wide business strategy designed to reduce costs and increase profitability by solidifying customer loyalty." How can you get that loyalty? Know your clients, and serve what they need. Once you've truly created that value in the eyes of the customer, it will become more difficult for them to make the decision to leave you and try someone new.

On a simple scale, be a good listener. Take notes, and keep them in a file or type them into a spreadsheet on your computer. Read through those notes every time you meet with the client. This preparation will enable you to make quick yet informed decisions on everything from cross-selling and upselling opportunities to target marketing strategies and competitive positioning tactics.

There is no one-size-fits-all, cookie-cutter format with your clients, and even though you are creating and implementing exercise programs, you would be wise to take advantage of the notes and experiences you have recorded to make each session truly an individualized event. This technique is using the concept of customer relationship management to your advantage. By getting to know them and individually tailoring their program, you will consistently exceed their expectations and secure that important long-term relationship.

#74: Community Relations

Community relations is a concept to consider incorporating into your business model—a concept that can generate good will and lead to more business. It's about being a good corporate citizen by providing value to the community that benefits both your business and the community.

The concept is simple: you find one or more community activities, causes, or organizations that share your values, and you participate with it in some way. It can start with establishing relationships with community partners—organizations that share your values and your vision for health or fitness.

For example, in the St. Louis area, hundreds of walks, runs, triathlons, and other fitness activities are, in many cases, fundraisers. The organizers of well-established events may have their fill of volunteers, sponsors, and booths. Smaller events, such as neighborhood runs, may not. Do your homework. Research fitness events that take place over the course of a year. Make some calls to find out the purpose of the event, the goals, the volunteer needs, or the opportunities to participate in a way that helps promote your business *and* helps fulfill their needs.

Your dedication to your community will be visible by what you support. If you have employees, brainstorm with them to determine the local charities, schools, or organizations they are interested in supporting. Remember, what you do and what you're involved in is a huge reflection on your business.

Your imagination is the limit. You can find many opportunities to get your business name out there and promote good will about your business and yourself. Even small events you participate in can reap major benefits. It may be a monetary donation or giving of your time, but it's another way to get your name and your business goodwill exposure.

The end result is simple: what you undertake in community relations will enhance your reputation and brand equity, expand your market, and—if you employ trainers—attract, motivate, and retain talented employees.

#75: Networking

It's an adage everyone has heard: you scratch my back; I'll scratch yours. In other words, I'll do something for you if you do something for me. On a non-business level, it can be a simple as helping a friend move a piece of furniture or weed a garden in return for a dinner and a movie. In business, it can be just as simple, and it starts with networking. Networking involves developing relationships that can reap rewards. It is meeting people who can be of help to you and being a help to them: a reciprocal relationship. You promote their business or service, and they promote yours.

Think about a time that you've gone into a local salon or downtown shop and right there, next to the cash register, are business cards or coupons for a business in the same neighborhood or for a business that offers a complementary service. With networking, you can expand your social network by initiating new relationships and finding potential clients from friends, business contacts, co-workers, acquaintances, and fellow members in professional and civic organizations.

Friends and family members can be a great source of new clients. Local chambers of commerce, special-interest groups, and business associations are a tremendous source of contacts. Do you provide a service from which someone can benefit? Expand your thoughts about who could refer clients to you: massage therapists, doctors, chiropractors, and local business owners. Contact the owner or manager, and talk about it. You will never know if you don't ask. Get out, and forge relationships!

With people you know well, it's easy to ask if they have any friends who are fitness-oriented and would be in need of your services. You can ask that they hand out your business cards, and in return, you can provide a free personal-training session, a fitness evaluation, or a massage. Next time you get your hair cut, talk with the stylist or owner about your area of expertise. Schedule a follow-up meeting at which you can brainstorm ways to help each other's business.

Getting involved in your local chamber of commerce is a must. Most have regularly scheduled meetings and networking events at which you can get to know local business owners. You also may piggy-back on some of their advertising and be listed in their local directories of businesses that belong to the local chamber.

Exercise

Think of everyone you know, even acquaintances, and categorize them. Which ones can you check off and contact quickly?

Family	*Friends*	*Acquaintances*	*Professional Organizations*
		Your doctor	Chamber of commerce
		Postal carrier	Lion's Club
		Hair stylist	

Stockbyte

#76: Managing Clients

When you think of the expectations of your clients, what they really want, it's your job to meet those expectations, or even exceed them. It's what managing your customers is all about.

You know that you want to deliver high-quality service to each and every client, every time you meet with them. As mentioned throughout the book, spending the time to listen to clients is a key to providing them with what they want.

If you haven't already, you likely will run into the challenge of scheduling customers when it's both convenient for them but also when it fits into your schedule of clients. Another challenge you'll face is when a client is late or does not show up for an appointment, which could make you late for your next session. It also can affect your bottom line.

Developing a policy to manage your customers, stating your terms regarding tardiness and no-shows, can help you in situations that may be uncomfortable to handle. A good time to present your terms is when you've signed a new client, but don't feel that you can't offer the same terms to existing clients. Be sure to include the information on your website.

Your clients will appreciate that you value their time as much as your own when they know you will be there consistently on time and are 100-percent committed to them. Even if you end up losing a client or two who are consistently late or no-shows, it's worth losing them to keep your good clients who are there week after week and on time. Fitness may be your passion, but it is not a charity. It is a business. Protect yourself at all costs.

#77: Finding a Mentor Who Matters

This may come as a blow, but no matter how much you think you may know, you can always learn more. Whether it is a new exercise or a change in your business operations, you always have room for improvement.

Sometimes, all it takes is a tiny change to an ad for a marketing campaign to catch fire. A tweak to your delivery during a session or some modifications to your boot camp could be the difference between a successful business and bankruptcy. Experience has to be earned, like a college degree, so whether you've been a personal trainer 10 years or 10 minutes, never look past the value of a good mentor.

"Should you need my assistance to talk about your career, please feel free to call me any time. I am a resource to you for life and, hopefully, vice versa." These were the words of the late Bob Lauman, a marketing professor at Webster University in St. Louis. What he gave his students went far beyond the classroom. Each person left with knowledge and a mind-set to pay it forward.

You can pay successful trainers to consult on your business, but there is something special about finding a mentor who has an altruistic purpose—someone who has already made it and is looking to help the next passionate entry into the field of fitness become a success.

Finding the right someone isn't easy. First and foremost, your passion and a drive to be the best will be recognized and will appeal to the right person. Second, you have to put yourself out there. Attend conferences, and become involved in local charities or organizations. Third, seek opportunity. And finally, be a friend first. If you are reciprocal and pay it forward, positive energy will surround you, and the world can become your oyster.

7

General Tips

iStockphoto/Thinkstock

#78: Getting Specific

As previously stated, a personal trainer who tries to be all things to all clients rarely succeeds in satisfying the client's needs. You just can't succeed when trying to be all things to everyone. It's not that you have to limit yourself to only one type of client, but there's a huge difference between training the fitness enthusiast looking to drop 10 pounds before swimsuit season and the athletic prospect making the jump from high school sports to the college game field.

When you've determined your niche—perhaps it's something at which you excel, such as running or cycling—figure out how to target that niche. Consider your area of expertise, and think about the type of client you intend to serve and the demographics of the people in your market area, such as annual household income, age, gender, race, and fitness goals. Then, take this market and segment it, focusing on those prospects who can benefit from your skills and experience.

Once you do this, you can build your marketing mix (product, price, promotion, and distribution plan) around the needs of this segmented population. If you are trained and certified in sports performance programs, stick to what you know and work with athletes. Do not venture into the affluent female baby boomer population whose fitness priorities are vastly different from your area of expertise.

Then, actively market to your specific group. Regardless of the population you plan to target, if you focus on and cater to their specific needs and wants, there's a good chance you will develop a following. The beginning will include some trial and error, but figure out what customer you plan to serve and serve them well.

iStockphoto/Thinkstock

#79: Persuading the Consumer

Persuading consumers to purchase your services or products entails a basic understanding of consumer buying behavior. Consumers have a certain amount of income with which they will pay their bills, taxes, and other necessities. What's left over is discretionary income. As a personal trainer, your income is based on the decision of consumers to spend a portion of their discretionary income on health and wellness. In most cases, consumers consider personal training as a luxury item.

Consumers have to eat and have a roof over the heads, and they will survive without a trainer—at least until their lack of action results in a massive heart attack in their mid-40s, but that is another story.

Your focus is to persuade consumers to buy your services with their discretionary income. The tips that follow will arm you with the knowledge you need when combating the nuances of consumer buying behavior:

- *Help your prospect solve the problem.* All consumers go through the same steps when making a purchase. They search for information, consider alternative purchases, evaluate the alternatives, and, finally, make the purchase. With personal training, clients want to connect with their trainer. Your job is to make the connection and convince the prospect to buy your services—not a book, DVD, or time with another trainer. It may take several meetings or conversations with these prospects, but let the clients tell you what they want. Then paint a picture for these prospects that entails everything they just told you. It is simple, yet incredibly effective.

- *Understand possible influences of decisions.* People buy based on situational, physiological, and social influences. Take the example of a 40-year-old woman who's told by her doctor that if she does not lose weight and lower her cholesterol, she'll have to start taking cholesterol-lowering medication. The social stigma attached with being overweight and on medication at such a young age will influence her behavior. Understanding these influences will help you develop a presentation to sell this prospect on you.

- *Remember that emotion drives behavior.* It drives the 44-year-old dad in the suburbs to ditch the mini-van and buy the Corvette. While good health and wellness are great, health can be a hard sell. Ask as many questions as you can until you find the prospect's hot buttons. Get to the root of why the prospect is sitting in front of you, and it won't take long before he signs on the dotted line.

Understand consumer buying behavior, and you will understand how to dominate your market.

#80: Identifying Wellness Opportunities for Businesses

Employee wellness programs have been documented to improve productivity, reduce absenteeism, and lower health-care claims. According to Employee Wellness USA:

- Coors Brewing Company states that it saves $5.50 for every dollar spent on wellness programming.
- Coca-Cola found that with 60 percent employee participation in its wellness programming, the company was able to save $500 per year per employee.
- On average, for every dollar spent for employee wellness programs, companies can expect to save $2.30 to $10.10.

The demand is there. Oftentimes, the seeds for developing wellness programming have already been planted by employees looking for stress management, smoking cessation, weight loss, or an on-site fitness facility. Companies of all sizes are investing in employee wellness, and if you want to tap into this growing segment of wellness, it's a matter of identifying the right person in the company to listen to your proposal. Sometimes, it comes down to good old-fashioned cold calling, or actively picking up the phone and drumming up business, and developing relationships with the right people.

A good place to start is with the human resources (HR) department. HR departments typically handle everything to do with employees, and in most cases, wellness initiatives. Take the opportunity to get your name to the right person, and prove that you have the products and services to not only meet their employees' needs, but also save them money.

About.com (http://sbinfocanada.about.com/cs/marketing/a/coldcall.htm) provides the following tips for making an initial call to a company:

- *Focus on the goal of the call*. The call is about getting an opportunity to make a sales pitch. It is not the time to make the sale.
- *Research your market and prospects*. Find out as much about the company as possible and their potential needs. Being familiar with them will give you an advantage.
- *Prepare an opening statement for your call*. A strong opening statement should include a greeting, an introduction, a reference point (something about the company), and the benefits of your product or service. Use your opening statement as the framework to help build the conversation. Know what you are going to say, and say it. For example, "Good afternoon, Mr. Smith. This is Robert Jones with XYZ Fitness. I read recently in the business journal that your company

is looking for ways to reduce costs related to health-insurance claims by your employees. XYZ Fitness specializes in developing programs designed to improve the health of your employees, increase productivity, reduce absenteeism, and ultimately save your company money. I would like to ask you a few questions to see if some of our programs might fit your specific needs."

It may seem uncomfortable making that first call, but persistence pays off, and it will only take one client saying "Yes" to add a new profit center to your personal-training business.

Creatas

#81: Opportunity Knocks

Everyone knows someone who seems to find good fortune at every turn. Those seemingly fortunate people are not lucky. They simply seek opportunity and possess a positive outlook on life.

Opportunity truly does lie around every corner. The difference between those who find and create opportunity and those who don't is recognizing and acting on situations. While it's impossible to control every aspect of the marketing environment, you can be proactive and find ways to make situations work to your advantage.

In an economic downturn, you may reason that your training volumes will decrease because consumers have less discretionary income. Makes sense, because training is considered a luxury, not a necessity. However, that is a reactive approach to the marketing environment, not a proactive mind-set. The way you approach your business and clients during an economic downturn, however, can greatly determine your livelihood and sustainability in good times and bad times.

If you do find that some of your clients discontinue training because of a change in income, you can proactively look for the opportunity and develop products and services with lower prices or target clients with larger pocketbooks. You don't want to blame environmental factors and let your business sink with the rest of the economy. It is possible to find customers everywhere, so always be on the lookout. Your next conversation with a stranger while in line at the local coffee shop could turn into a paying customer. After all, if they are willing to spend $5 on a cup of coffee, they probably have the discretionary income for a trainer.

The point is simple. Don't let circumstances beyond your control determine your success. Be observant, have a positive attitude, and proactively seek and capitalize on opportunity. The next person you interact with today could be the one who opens a brand new door for you.

#82: Building Loyalty Through Ethics

Your own ethical behavior, as well as that of the people you employ, can easily make or break your reputation. Ethics relates to individual and group decisions—judgments about what is right or wrong in a particular decision-making situation (Pride and Ferrell, 2006). Simply put, it's the concept of right and wrong behavior. The ethical (or unethical) behavior of a business owner can have a profound effect on his success.

When an organization and its employees behave ethically, current and potential customers are likely to develop a positive attitude about the company and its services and products. When the customers see ethical behavior on a consistent basis, it can further build loyalty to your products and services. Conversely, unethical behavior can result in a loss of trust, and therefore, lost customers. An extreme example of unethical behavior is the Enron debacle that unfolded late in 2001, and everyone has seen trainers who will say anything to get the sale—even if it is a lie or something that could be potentially harmful to the client.

Ethical issues can arise in any of the four Ps of the marketing mix:
- *Product*: Verify the safety or performance of what is promised.
- *Price*: Be honest when determining your pricing. Do not set prices based solely on how much customers are willing to pay for the services or products you provide.
- *Promotion*: Do not encourage clients to purchase more than they need or can afford in their effort to achieve or maintain a certain lifestyle or image.
- *Placement (distribution)*: Have the product or service available at the time(s) promised.

The American Marketing Association's Code of Ethics includes six ethical values that should be embraced and practiced:
- *Honesty*: Means being truthful and forthright in dealing with customers and stakeholders
- *Responsibility*: Involves accepting the consequences of marketing decisions and strategies
- *Fairness*: Has to do with trying to balance the needs of the buyer with the interests of the seller
- *Respect*: Addresses the basic human dignity of all stakeholders
- *Openness*: Focuses on creating transparency in marketing operations
- *Citizenship*: Involves a strategic focus on fulfilling the economic, legal, philanthropic, and societal responsibilities that serve stakeholders

While you may already embrace these values, take some time to develop your own code of ethics, and display it for everyone to see. Add it to your business cards. Use it in your advertising. Make it short yet meaningful. St. Louis Children's Hospital has a simple but telling statement that is at the very heart of what they do: "St. Louis Children's Hospital will do what is right for children." It's ingrained in the organizational culture, and every employee and patient family knows and believes it to be true. The hospital is ranked among the top pediatric hospitals in the United States. The website www.business-ethics.com is an online magazine of corporate responsibility and ethics. Check it out for examples and education for companies that want to operate responsibly and demonstrate ethical values.

No matter what, even if it means not making the sale, always conduct your personal-training business the right way. You may miss out on a sale here and there, but in the long run you will position yourself in the business community as a personal trainer who has character and integrity—both of which are invaluable to a business in any category. Trust is important. Never give your clients or your target market any reason to think otherwise.

Jupiterimages

#83: Creating Quality

Rule #1: The training session is never about you. Got your attention? Good. Your business is about the people paying you their good money to have you lead them to the promised land. They are not paying you to hear about your job, friends, significant other, or dog. You were hired to meet their needs.

Any fitness professional can write a fitness program and count reps. There is a difference between a personal-training session and a quality personal-training session. The client's perception of quality starts with you, and it needs to start today with a few simple steps:

- *Get to know your clients*. How much do you know about your clients aside from the information collected in their fitness assessment? Are they married? Do they have a dog, kids, a job they love? Everyone says they want to lose weight and tone muscle in an initial consultation, but have you made an effort to understand why your client has gained 15 pounds in two years?
- *Listen to your clients*. The saying "You have two ears and one mouth" should be your philosophy when creating a quality personal-training session for your clients. Something as simple as helping an overweight housewife link emotional eating and subsequent weight issues with the stress she is under will create a total experience for her. If you listen long enough, your customers will give all the answers you need to create the experience they desire.
- *Empathize with your customers*. Resist the urge to blurt out an answer that will fix their problems.
- *Make every session memorable*. Have you ever been to Walt Disney World®? Can you remember the first professional baseball game you attended? Chances are you can because of the positive experience. Strive to create the same experience in your training sessions for your clients.

When your clients realize that the session is really about them, not only will you learn what makes that person tick, but you can educate, support, and motivate more effectively. Listen more than you talk. Ask the right questions that will lead you down the path to the answers.

Once you learn how to create a quality experience with one client, duplicate it. You will have crossed the line from designing exercise programs to being the trainer known for creating quality personal-training programs.

#84: Service Quality

The definition of quality is subjective. Each consumer has his own interpretation of quality. As a fitness professional, you should be concerned with the quality of service you provide. The delivery of high-quality services is what customers seek, whether those services are fitness or dry cleaning.

If you think that your interpretation of the quality of your service matters most, think again. The quality of service is the customers' perception of how well the service meets their needs or expectations. It's not what you think of your own service. This perception is a fatal flaw by many trainers in the industry: thinking they know more than the client. Clients are paying you, so it is wise to perform at a level that exceeds their expectations.

Put yourself in the role of a customer for a moment. Say, for example, you need stationery, business cards, and a newsletter printed. Your desired level of service—what you rank as service quality—is a job done according to the date and time you request and with perfect printing. When your order is delivered a day late and is printed with the wrong shade of blue ink, you'll accept the order, but you're not thrilled with it. The printer's job has affected your interpretation of service quality, while the printer may think a late delivery with a shade off on the color is perfectly acceptable.

Your customers are seeking a positive experience and adjust their expectations accordingly. Some service qualities customers will use to evaluate you include:
- *Your appearance*: Are you clean shaven, neat in appearance, and with clothes well fitting?
- *Your reliability*: Are you on time, is your billing accurate, and do you perform the services you say you will?
- *Your responsiveness*: Do you return phone calls and e-mails promptly?
- *Your attitude*: Do you give your client the energy and support they are paying for and do it to the best of your ability?
- *Your assurance*: Are you knowledgeable about your industry? Do you have the skills you claim?
- *Your empathy*: Do you listen to the customers' needs and care about their interests?

Providing consistent, quality service is important. When the perception of quality begins to deteriorate, consumer expectations will change with negative results and you may lose your client. When you enter a session or have any client contact, it should be your mission to leave that client thinking "Wow!" Anything less is not acceptable.

#85: Understanding Your Customers' Perception of Value

Value means something different to just about everyone, but in many cases, consumers are looking for the biggest bang for their dollar. They may consolidate errands to save on gas, they pay attention to which grocery stores offer the best prices, and they strive to live on less without sacrificing the things that are important to them. Therefore, fitness professionals must understand and strive to reach and, if possible, exceed their client's expectations. Personal training and fitness tend to be a want rather than a need, so you must prove you are worth the investment.

Value is subjective and individual. Each of your customers sees the benefit of what you do in relation to the cost of your service. Your job is to understand each client's perception of value and deliver what they seek. Offering an exercise plan and on-the-spot motivation may not be enough.

Try creating additional value that will appeal to your entire client base without sacrificing huge amounts of time and money, such as:

- *Send your clients a monthly e-newsletter*. Look online, and you will see stories, recipes, issues, and trends all relating to health and fitness. Use those stories to spark ideas, in conjunction with your knowledge, to develop a user-friendly, content-rich newsletter.
- *Build follow-up e-mails and telephone calls into your pricing*. Too often, trainers believe that they can only make money while in the physical presence of a client. Not true. Most clients like the extra touch of an e-mail or telephone call to check on progress or for motivation. If nothing else, it shows you are serious about their investment in you and that you are willing to go the extra mile. Factor in what your time is worth, and add it to the overall price of your session or personal-training packages.
- *Offer freebies*. This may cost you time and money, but if you have a client who has displayed loyalty, throw in a free session. Recognize birthdays. If you have logo apparel for your business, toss them a free t-shirt. What little it will cost you in time or money will reap benefits for you in customer loyalty.
- *Create a referral rewards program*. Hotels do it. So do airlines. Offer one free session for every referral your client sends your way. Your clients can be your best advertisement, so offer them something in return for a referral. You will gain new business, and your clients profit as well.
- *Diversify*. Become a source of knowledge and a resource for your clients. Free sources like mypyramid.gov and other websites allow you to download nutritional

information that will help your clients combine exercise with proper nutrition. Develop relationships with physicians, dietitians, massage therapists, and chiropractors you trust so when your client is in need, you can save them time and energy looking for the right provider. Being able to refer someone on the spot will increase your value because you are helping them simplify their lives.

Everyone's perception of value is subjective. Take the time to understand your client's perception of value, develop systems in your business that will enhance your value, and you will beat your competition time and again.

Hemera/Thinkstock

#86: Duplicate Yourself

As mentioned earlier, trading time for money and doing only one-on-one sessions will limit your income. Even if you charge $100 an hour and train six clients a day, you'll always be making $600 a day.

Not that $600 per day is bad money, but just try to maintain six clients a day with no cancellations, vacations, or sick days. However, if you hire a trainer or two to help train your clients, you can duplicate yourself and not worry so much about taking the occasional vacation or sick day.

Following are some things to consider when hiring a trainer to subcontract for you:

- *Establish a service agreement.* You can find numerous examples on the Internet and in personal-training manuals. Draft an agreement, and hire an attorney to fine-tune it. Table 86-1 gives an example of a service agreement. Include payment terms, no-compete clauses, and renewal and termination terms. Trainers you hire should carry their own liability insurance, and clearly state in the agreement you are not responsible if they injure themselves while training a client.
- *Discuss the tax implications with your accountant.* Nothing is worse than finding out after the fact you did something wrong and owe Uncle Sam a large portion of your earnings.
- *Be particular about who you hire.* The trainers you hire must share your training and fitness philosophies. After all, this is your business and your brand. If you have a degree in an exercise-science-related field along with a reputable certification, then anyone you hire to train your clients should have the same credentials.
- *Determine a rate that will enable you to still make a profit after paying another trainer.* If you charge $50 a session, you certainly can't pay your subcontractors the same amount. When you a drawing up an agreement with your subcontractors, be sure you are both comfortable with the rate charged per session and the rate the trainer will receive for each session.

With the help of your attorney and accountant, do your homework, and ensure that your training business truly reflects your philosophies, regardless of who's training your clients. Get the right people in place, and realize the power of duplicating yourself.

XYZ Fitness, LLC
Independent Contractor Agreement

Name: _____

Address: _____ City/Zip: _____

Telephone: _____

Social Security #: _____

This Independent Contractor Agreement ("Agreement") is entered into as of the ___ day of _____, 20____, by and between _____ ("Independent Contractor") and XYZ Fitness, LLC, a Missouri limited liability company. XYZ Fitness, LLC and Independent Contractor agree as follows:

Services: Independent Contractor shall perform personal training sessions for clients referred to Independent Contractor by XYZ Fitness, LLC.

Location of Job:

Billing and Payment: Independent Contractor shall bill XYZ Fitness, LLC for the services provided in the prior month. Each invoice shall describe the services and time expended in such detail as may reasonably be required by XYZ Fitness, LLC. XYZ Fitness, LLC shall pay Independent Contractor 60 percent of each training personal-training session Independent Contractor provides for clients XYZ Fitness, LLC refers to Independent Contractor. XYZ Fitness, LLC shall pay Independent Contractor for the services rendered in the previous month by the 5th of each month.

Terms and Conditions:
1. Independent Contractor shall perform all services hereunder as an independent contractor, and not as an agent, officer, or employee of XYZ Fitness, LLC.
2. Independent Contractor shall purchase and maintain comprehensive general liability insurance in amounts which are standard in the industry and shall provide proof of such insurance upon request. Independent Contractor shall not be entitled to receive employment insurance, workers' compensation, or any other insurance coverage by XYZ Fitness, LLC.
3. Independent Contractor shall not, under any circumstance, assign this contract to another provider.
4. This Agreement may be terminated by XYZ Fitness, LLC or Independent Contractor upon giving three weeks written notice to the other party.
5. Independent Contractor shall not hold XYZ Fitness, LLC or its directors, officers, or employees responsible for any injuries or accidents and agrees to indemnify, defend, and hold harmless XYZ Fitness, LLC, its directors, officers, and employees against any liability, claims, damages, injuries, accidents, or loss, including but not limited to claims for workers' compensation, arising out of the services provided by Independent Contractor.
6. If Independent Contractor is ill or unable to provide personal-training services, he must notify XYZ Fitness, LLC within 24 hours of a scheduled personal-training session.
7. XYZ Fitness, LLC reserves the right to terminate this contract immediately for cause.
8. Independent Contractor gives consent to XYZ Fitness, LLC to use any photographs, pictures, or videotape of him for future promotional or marketing efforts.
9. Upon the expiration/termination of this Agreement, Independent Contractor shall not (i) train clientele of XYZ Fitness, LLC; nor (ii) employ, attempt to employ, or solicit for employment any employee of XYZ Fitness, LLC for one calendar year from the expiration/termination of this Agreement.
10. Independent Contractor shall supply, at his expense, all equipment and supplies to accomplish the job agreed to be performed unless otherwise agreed in writing.
11. The term of this Agreement shall commence on the date first written above and shall continue until terminated by either party.

Owner XYZ Fitness, LLC:_____ Date:_____

Independent Contractor:_____ Date:_____

Table 86-1. Service agreement sample

#87: Supplements and Nutritional Products

As discussed in previous sections, the trainer who understands the importance of multiple income streams will achieve success by generating revenues above and beyond one-on-one training sessions. One great way to supplement your personal-training income is through a consumable product such as supplements and nutritional products. The two go hand in hand.

Americans in general have poor diets, so you can assume that some of your clients fall into that category. Pre- and post-workout nutrition can help a client achieve greater results faster. There is a market for adding supplements to your product mix, but before you go out and invest in any supplements, consider some important points:

- *Know your limits.* Unless you are a registered dietitian, you shouldn't be providing detailed nutrition advice. Items such as whey protein shakes, multi-vitamins, and fish oil are safe for most individuals, and there is science to back their efficacy. Avoid products that claim to burn fat, increase metabolism, or promise anything to good to be true. Your first rule should be to do no harm, so make sure the products you sell follow the same mantra.
- *Check out Web-based fulfillment programs.* Many wholesalers of nutritional products are available to help you set up an online store using their technology and inventory (thereby eliminating the need to turn your garage into a warehouse for protein powder and fish oil). Typically, a fee is associated for the service, depending on how much you sell. If the terms are right, it is a win-win situation. Lonestar Distribution and Europa Sports Products are two wholesalers that have Web fulfillment programs.
- *If you don't take it, don't sell it.* If you don't take or believe in the product, you will lack credibility. Customers want to know if a product will work for them, so your personal experience and endorsement are valuable to them.
- *If your client doesn't need it, don't push it.* Some of your clients may have great diets that don't warrant supplementation. You will get more from your customers when you run your business with honor and integrity. If the product isn't for them, do not become the used-car salesman just to make a sale.

Be sure to have in-depth conversations with your clients about their diets and eating habits to determine whether they'd benefit from the supplements you choose to offer. Do a good job of educating them on your products, and let them make the decision without pressure. They will appreciate your expertise as well as your interest in their overall health.

#88: Building Your Business on the CICE Principles

When operating a personal-training business, one thing is for certain: all the marketing tips in the world cannot help the shady businessperson with poor ethics and no passion. Clients eventually see through the trainers who are in it solely for the money, although they may be able to fool their clients for a while.

Personal training is your job, but without passion and ethics, you will lack the intangible factor that helps clients exceed their goals. Trainers who use pushy sales tactics and half-truths may get clients first, but if you operate your business on the CICE principles (character, integrity, continuity, and enthusiasm), eventually their clients will turn to you.

- *Character*: Trainers who display character will always win out over those who use sleazy sales tactics to gain business. For example, a trainer with character isn't going to push the high-priced vitamins to a client who has excellent eating habits and does not need supplementation.
- *Integrity*: A trainer with integrity has the ability to adhere to a high moral and ethical code, no matter what the situation. Clients who share personal and private details about their lives trust that you will keep that information confidential.
- *Continuity*: The methods by which you deliver an individual client's service should be consistent. Once you determine what a client wants and needs, building continuity in the way you deliver that service will create a flow and a process that can be repeated every time you meet. Clients know if you are winging it. Be prepared, and have a plan for every session and beyond.
- *Enthusiasm*: Enthusiasm cannot be faked. When you've agreed to a 6 a.m. training session, you'd better be peppy and 100 percent into them. When you're into the session, your client will be into the session. If you're not, it won't take long before that client is history.

A successful business is much more than marketing concepts. Your passion and ethics matter most. Once your reputation is tarnished, it is hard to remove that mark. Operate under the CICE principles, and you'll never put yourself or your business in the position to be questioned.

#89: How to Run a Marketing Campaign

You don't have to be a marketing genius to run an effective marketing campaign. The right combination of a product, idea, or service, coupled with an awareness of customer wants and needs, topped off with a good idea are the basics of any good campaign. And, of course, you need to promote.

You can witness a great example of an effective marketing campaign from start to finish with the release of a blockbuster movie. First are rumors, and then teasers and Internet chat rooms. Next, clips of scenes and full-length trailers are shown in movie theaters and posted on the Internet. Finally, the movie premieres with celebrity interviews and photo sessions and maybe even a cross-promotion with a restaurant so that everywhere you turn, you see, hear, and feel the buzz.

The entire process doesn't happen overnight and may continue for up to a year from the start of a campaign to the premiere of the film. You can use the same techniques for running marketing campaigns for your business. Following are some examples to start generating a plan:

- *Come up with a concept.* Getting clients in January is easy. Getting clients in July is another story. A marketing concept or promotion, such as "Renew Your Resolutions," may generate the same New Year's emotional desires and motivation for fitness and generate some new business.
- *Tease your market.* If you wait until July to spring this idea into action, you will have created zero buzz or excitement. Start promoting the idea a couple months in advance. A brief statement in your May e-newsletter or flyer, such as, "Achieving your resolution is closer than you think," will generate interest and curiosity.
- *The month before you launch, be more descriptive in your e-newsletter or other marketing and advertising.* While you may not be ready to unveil the entire concept, start generating excitement. Promote your concept in every e-mail and in every exercise session and article you send. Show enthusiasm, and do not be afraid to talk it up. If you are excited about it, your clients and prospects will be as well.
- *Launch the campaign.* Offering a free training session for every five sessions purchased or running an incentive contest are great ways to get your clients renewed and ready to pick up where they left off. If you sell supplements, offer a free tub of whey protein for every 20 sessions purchased, linking the importance of nutrition and recovery and opening up another revenue stream. You are convincing your clients and prospect that now is the time to "Renew Your Resolutions," so get creative.

The only rule is that there are no rules. Develop an idea, and run with it. The only thing stopping you from an effective marketing campaign is you.

#90: How's Your Posture?

Lester Maevers owned and operated the IGA grocery store in Jackson, Missouri, for more than 30 years. One of Mr. Maevers' pet peeves was workers on the clock standing with their hands in their pockets, and for good reason. He concluded that:

- Employees cannot work with their hands in their pockets.
- Customers, and management, will perceive these employees as lazy.

Obviously, actions speak volumes. When training clients, you may not think twice about leaning against a piece of equipment, crossing your arms, or simply standing with your hands in your pockets. However, your actions are telling a story about you as a trainer.

Proxemics is the study of body language, and it can tell quite a bit about you as a trainer. It can also help gauge your clients' and prospects' attitudes. For example, if a new prospect is closing herself off to you by crossing her arms, angling her body away from you, or increasing the distance between you, something is awry with your delivery. Conversely, you can be guaranteed that the client who's smiling, making eye contact, and facing you is interested in more information about your services.

You also need to be aware of how clients and prospects perceive you. Be sure to master the following nonverbal cues to put your clients at ease with you:

- *Always face your client in an open manner.* Do not cross your arms, put your hands in your pockets, or lean.
- *Smile.* This goes without saying, but if you appear happy and positive, those feelings will rub off without you saying a word.
- *Make eye contact.* Talk directly with your clients while maintaining eye contract. People who will not look others in the eye can be perceived as untrustworthy.
- *Be on the same level as the client.* If the client is doing a floor exercise, kneel beside him. Do not stand over him; it can be intimidating. Make him as comfortable as possible, and show your client you are focused on him.

Marketing isn't just something that happens on paper. It happens before, during, and after any customer interaction you have. Be aware of your body language at all times to ensure that the volumes your actions are speaking are positive.

#91: Learning to Adapt

Trainers who try to be all things to all people usually end up satisfying no one. Find your niche or area of expertise, and run with it. That's not to say, however, that within your niche, you won't have a variety of personalities to contend with. Your ability to find common ground with each client will enable you to take your interactions beyond reps and form.

People who can find common ground with strangers and adjust their personality to external factors have a distinct ability to work with a variety of people from custodians to royalty. Why? Because no matter what, they will have something they can talk about.

If you weren't born with that natural gift, and you're certainly not alone, you can learn how to relate to any client who comes your way. Before you begin your next session, try the following tips:

- *Read something.* Check out the headlines online or read the newspaper. Look at the business section, sports page, and local headlines so you're informed about current events and can talk about topics other than fitness.
- *Really listen to your clients.* This may take several sessions, but if you are spending more time in your sessions talking about you, something is wrong. Your focus should be on your clients, their session, and whatever it is they want to talk about within the limits of good taste. It is always about the client.
- *Ask open-ended questions.* If your client just got back from vacation, get them talking about their trip. Most of the time, people like to talk about themselves, and aside from helping them tone their muscles, your sessions are a great opportunity for them to talk.
- *Write down what you learn.* If in your sessions you learn that a client's son will be the starting pitcher in the upcoming Little League game, be sure to ask how he did during your next session. It will not only show you listen to your clients, it will show you care. Keeping an informal log will help jog your memory.

#92: A Little Attitude Goes a Long Way

Your attitude is the one thing you can control. Nobody can be on his "A" game 100 percent of the time. Everyone gets tired, burnt out, or will find their mind wandering while working with clients. It is human nature, but your ability to perform when it matters most, both your fitness expertise and attitude, will give your client the best value for their investment.

World-renowned fitness instructor, trainer, and author Lawrence Biscontini believes that when you are working with clients, standing at the front desk of your facility, or are anywhere a client, member, or guest can see you, you are on stage. The clients are paying you to perform, so when it is time for their session, regardless of your mood, you must be in the now and completely focused on them. For example, if you had an argument with your significant other, you should have checked those emotions at the door when you took off your "personal issue" hat and put on your "personal trainer" hat.

If the waitress working hard for tips comes to the table with a sour face, mopes as she takes your order, and then, because she is distracted by outside issues, messes up your order, you would be very unhappy with your service. If that same waitress, despite her personal issues that day, is able to put on a smile and be in the now, her customers will never know she's having a bad day.

Your clients have hired you, not your personal problems, and while it is hard to be upbeat at times, a sour-puss attitude can kill your business. No matter how good your training skills are, the "personal" in personal trainer is equally as important as your exercise science skills.

Be aware of your moods, energy level, and attitude, keep your problems to yourself, and be the positive influence your clients want and deserve in their personal trainer. Your attitude can make the difference between a satisfied client and one who's looking for a new trainer.

#93: Think About the Big Picture

This book has introduced the importance of marketing plans, target markets, and business skills needed to improve your personal-training business; however, the one thing a book cannot do is rewire your brain to think outside the box. But simply looking at things a little differently may change your "big picture" perceptions.

Being a visionary and finding something you can latch onto and use to build your business is as much an art as a science. Take this book, for example. Following an observation that the market is flooded with marketing books, but not one is focused on marketing for personal trainers, that observation was transformed.

Anyone could have written this book. What you see when you open your front door every morning, or when you walk through the front doors of your gym or training studio, and then how you act on it, will determine success or failure.

Learning to follow through on that moment when you think to yourself, "That idea just might work," can turn some of the best ideas into realities. You will never know if that idea or concept would have worked if it remains on the shelf. The fun part is that if you implement it and it fails, so what? Find another idea, and run with it.

Anyone in sales will tell you that their life is one big rejection with a few moments of success. Think of the fitness-equipment rep who is turned down day after day, but all it takes is a contract with the new 40,000-square-foot facility in town to turn a bad day into a career year.

Turn the ordinary into the extraordinary by changing same 10-week weight-loss program into something exciting by changing the name, format, flow, and flavor. You know weight loss is about calories out versus calories in, but that doesn't mean your programming has to be boring. Infuse some fun into your programs.

Late-night television is full of infomercials starring trainers who have stamped their names on products or created a workout DVD and is now generating a phenomenal living by selling the same piece of exercise equipment you use every day. That could be you selling a product on late-night TV. Tomorrow when you step outside, put on your marketing goggles before your feet hit the pavement. You will be amazed what you see.

#94: Generating Ideas

Everyone's been there. You are stuck. All of your creative juices, flow, and energy seem to have left. That one good idea to jump-start your business eludes you, even though you've racked your brain for days. Sometimes, taking a step back is all you need.

While trying to generate an idea for your next class or workout may result in sleepless nights, try starting anew with an open mind, and your eyes open to the world around you. A simple observance may serve as a lightening rod for the next hot concept in personal training, but only if you're paying attention.

You may be inspired while working out, watching TV, training a client, or grabbing a latte at the local coffee shop. Following are some tips to help unleash your creativity to develop a circuit for that next class or client or even the next new trend or product in fitness:

- *Listen to your clients*. Their wants and needs can trigger concepts that will build your business and satisfy their desires.
- *Observe life with a discerning eye*. The next idea you generate could be in the doctor's office, grocery store, or car wash.
- *Write it down*. Always keep a notepad handy because ideas can easily be lost when they're not written down. You just never know what may turn into gold.
- *Attend conferences*. Conferences are a financial investment (talk with your accountant on how to write off educational expenses), but they feature the latest trends and research in a non-competitive setting. Learn, absorb, and network with other attendees.
- *Develop relationships with others in the field and find a good mentor.*
- *Stay abreast of everything in the business environment, from the economy to politics, both locally and in the country.* Understanding the dynamic environment in which you live will enable you to be proactive and develop as the environment evolves.

Get your creative juices flowing by having an awareness of what is happening around you. That next interaction, event, or circumstance may generate ideas for expanding your business and inspiring your clients and—who knows?—may be the next trend in fitness.

#95: Taking an Idea for a Test Drive

Launching a new product or service is a lot like test-driving a new vehicle. Before blindly investing a great deal of money into an idea, a company will perform a detailed analysis, make sure it has all the bells and whistles consumers want, and then test the product with a group of consumers.

Companies large and small will test products with a chosen target population before launching on a national scale. They want to gauge how the product or service will be received. A small-scale test launch will typically feature a full roll-out of the product, including the four Ps of the market mix, in the test market.

Advantages of test marketing include the ability to:
• Gather valuable information on customer response, marketing channels, and distribution issues.
• Involve customers, which will make them feel more invested in the service or product.
• Assess customer attitudes toward your service and your competitors.
• Test the effectiveness of your advertising efforts on a smaller scale.

Before moving forward with launching a product or service, as well as a test launch, be sure to have a clear picture in mind of what you're trying to accomplish. While your service or product launch may not be large-scale, instituting the concept of test marketing in your personal-training business may be the difference between a huge success and money down the drain.

To get started, choose a small segment of your clientele or target market. Make sure you not only have the product ready to go, but the pricing, distribution, and promotion plans set.

Next, roll out your test launch. Whether you're adding an early morning boot camp at your local park, subcontracting to local wedding planners to help brides-to-be tone up, or offering supplements, what matters is that you're testing to determine if it will be financially viable.

Finally, take notes. This is the time to see if any part of that product—including the promotion, pricing, and distribution—needs altering. Perhaps everything is great, but no one will buy because of the pricing. The test market is the time to fine tune everything about that product and determine if it will work. If it doesn't, walk away from it. If it's a rousing success in the test market, roll it out full scale.

With the results from your test market in hand, you can move forward with your full product launch with confidence, or if necessary, refine your marketing strategy.

#96: Educate Yourself About the World of Business

The importance of education can't be underestimated. It provides knowledge, equips individuals with information to make decisions throughout life, and contributes to the economic growth of the country. Your education as a fitness professional shouldn't have stopped when you finished college and certification. Successful businesspeople are students for life.

Tim Cluny, an independent distributor for Advanced Exercise Equipment, a commercial equipment sales and service organization, begins his day reading fitness and business journals. In his 20-plus years in the fitness industry, he has made it his job to be informed, both in his field and in the world of business. He learns every nuance, both positive and negative, about the equipment he sells, as well as that of his competitors. His vast knowledge and understanding of all areas in business enable him to answer client questions and provide unparalleled service.

If you don't already, subscribe to one or two fitness journals to keep up on the latest in the field. These publications will keep you on top of trends and science, will help you become a better trainer, and provide answers to questions your clients may ask.

Subscribing to a national business journal, such as the *Wall Street Journal* or *Newsweek* will keep you on top of business trends in all industries. Most major cities also have local business publications. As a business owner, knowledge of the world around you is power. Educating yourself on terminology, concepts and the economy can help you make better business decisions. Check out the online versions of a variety of business publications before investing in a subscription.

Knowledge is power, which can set you apart from your competitors and impact the success of your personal-training business. You can never learn too much.

Hemera/Thinkstock

#97: Making the Most of Your Time

Your time is perishable. You cannot store unused time for future use. If you have an open slot at 4 p.m. and don't fill that slot with a paying client, you lose that chunk of potential revenue-generating time forever. Cancellations and no-shows are a part of life for professionals in service industries, and while having a cancellation policy helps, a contingency plan is paramount to making money.

You likely have a list of business tasks for each week or month that you build time into your schedule to complete. Your contingency plan or to-do list can be the extras you'd love to do, but have not found the time to take on. Some of the concepts in this book can be on that contingency list. Spend some down time developing, honing, and working on items on your to-do list. Perhaps you've considered starting a blog, but haven't found the time to research the concept, or you've wanted to write an article on a client success story.

The next time a client cancels, have that to-do list or that contingency plan ready to go. When you have a contingency plan, gaps between clients can be productive. Think of those times as ways to increase the revenues flowing into your business. Be aggressive, and look for ways to build your business around every corner, including making the most out of downtime.

Jupiterimages

#98: When to Call in the Experts

As a personal trainer, you have worked hard to get your education and credentials. The concepts presented in this book will help you understand how implementing marketing concepts and theory will increase revenues and position your brand to succeed.

There are, however, certain things about your business that you should leave to the experts—namely accounting and legalities, and for good reason. First, because these are not your areas of expertise, you will end up spending an inordinate amount of time on activities that do not generate revenues. Second, making a legal or accounting mistake may cost you a lot of money. You are the expert in health and fitness, so it makes sense to seek professional help for accounting and legal matters.

In addition to filing your taxes, an accountant can guide you through tax implications of employees, and the advantages of filing your business as a limited liability corporation, partnership, or corporation. An accountant also can advise on how to handle subcontractors, tax issues that arise from selling goods such as exercise equipment and supplements, and keep you abreast of changes in tax law. A lawyer will draw up any legal papers for incorporating or establishing a partnership, and handle contracts, trademark issues, liability waivers, and other documents vital to your business.

Finding the right professionals to work with can be as easy as talking with your friends, clients, or professionals you do business with and asking for some referrals. Be sure to do your homework on possible candidates, ask for and follow up with references, and plan to interview several candidates before making a decision. When you interview them, be specific about your needs and how much you will need their services.

As a business owner, you should have a solid understanding of how to professionally and legally run your business, but trust the professionals with the financial and legal aspect of your business to take care of accounting and legal issues. It's what they do for a living, and their expertise will save you time and money in the long run.

#99: Sometimes It Is Who You Know

As the saying goes, "It isn't *what* you know; it's *who* you know." Whether that's accurate 15 percent or 100 percent of the time, it is true that many business partnerships are relationship based. Just open any textbook on sales, and you will realize the power in relationships.

Those who understand the power of relationships are ahead of the curve. It is a common thread in the world of business. People are more likely to participate in a business transaction with someone they know and like. From clients and prospects, to wholesalers and vendors you use to support your business, every interaction is an opportunity for a relationship.

Having relationships that will solidify your business can be as easy as starting a conversation with a smile. When you're meeting prospects or longtime clients, smile and ask them how they're doing. And mean it. If you are fake or are simply going through the motions, it will come across that way, so you may have to work at it.

Have some fun. Many business deals are finalized on golf courses. There's something about camaraderie that makes people feel at ease and establishes trust, which is impossible if you don't work on your relationship skills. Laughter has the power to heal and relax even the tightest of situations.

Pharmaceutical reps get it. They know that if you can get the desk clerk (the gatekeeper in all physician's offices) to like them, they have a better chance at getting that doctor to use their product. If you are well liked by your clients, you are providing more to them than a person who compiles exercises and counts reps. You are giving them a complete experience, and happy clients are clients who are happy to refer their friends…to you. That is the power of relationships!

#100: Are You Covered?

Paying your taxes and using the appropriate documents are important to ensure that you're adhering to the legal regulations in your state or places of business, but one very important piece of protection could be the difference between survival and failure: liability insurance.

As a personal trainer, your number-one rule when working with your clients should be: do no harm. No one goes into a session thinking, "Wow, let's cause an injury today," but in reality, it will happen eventually. Sadly, society is litigious, and even if you strictly adhere to proper training protocols, some clients will sue. Without liability insurance, you could lose more than a client; you could lose everything you own and more.

Today, a growing number of insurance providers offer products for personal trainers. Get covered. Be sure you read the details of the policy. It never hurts to go with reputation when making your choice.

Both the American College of Sports Medicine and the National Strength and Conditioning Association offer members the opportunity to purchase liability policies. Reputation is important because this is your life and livelihood you are dealing with. Finally, look at price. It's tempting to go with the cheapest policy, but if that policy does not provide adequate coverage, it isn't worth the paper it is printed on. Sometimes, it pays to pay a little more. Do your research.

Any time a client is injured, it is a blow to the ego and your reputation. However, if you have taken steps to protect your business and its assets, the equation of no insurance + a torn bicep = disaster for your career won't happen.

#101: Pulling It All Together

You are more than a personal trainer. You are a marketer. On any given day, you will participate in product design, customer service, sales, advertising, branding, and more. The list goes on. Every time you meet with a client, talk with a prospect or business associate, and even walk into a gym, you represent your business.

The last 100 tips have presented you with a wealth of knowledge to improve your marketing and business skills that will set you apart from trainers who rely on luck to get them through. Becoming aware of marketing concepts and business terminology will make you a better business owner. That is why this book was conceptualized. There are great programs cranking out very skilled fitness professionals who lack the business education they need to succeed. Much of that business education can be learned right here, and there are a couple ways to approach the concepts:

- Follow the book from start to finish. It is laid out as a paint-by-numbers process to help you understand how to get started and progress from that point.
- Latch on to one or two concepts at a time, and slowly implement them into your business model.

However you decide to proceed, you're taking action by reading this book and following the concepts. What truly separates the successful from those who fail is the ability to take action and knowing that when you get knocked down, you'll get back up and continue on in your intended direction.

Finally, this book was modeled after the core definition of the marketing concept, which means you are putting everything into creating the ultimate customer experience, one customer at a time. If nothing else, always focus on that one concept. Your customers are the lifeblood of your business.

Good luck, and happy marketing!

Recommended Websites and Blogs

The websites listed in this section may serve as resources, as well as examples of sites that can provide information and inspiration for your personal-training business.

American College of Sports Medicine
www.acsm.org

American Marketing Association
www.marketingpower.com

Lawrence Biscontini
www.findlawrence.com

BNET
www.bnet.com

Business Plans
www.bplans.com

Club Industry.com—The Online Source
for Fitness Business Professionals
www.clubindustry.com

Entrepreneur
www.entrepreneur.com

Entrepreneur Website
www.zeromillion.com

FedStats
www.fedstats.gov

Forbes Online
www.forbes.com

The International Health, Racquet &
Sportsclub Association
cms.ihrsa.org

The Marketing Blog
http://marketing-expert.blogspot.com

Marketing Plans
ducttapemarketing.com
marketitright.com

A Trail Runner's Blog
runtrails.blogspot.com

References and Recommended Reading

You are what you read. Books and periodicals on marketing, business, and fitness are great ways to learn more about the four Ps of marketing to help build your business, remain current on fitness practices, and gain knowledge of the world of business. The books and publications that follow are just a few resources to fuel your brain power.

Books

Berkowitz, E. (2004). *Essentials of Health Care Marketing*. Sudbury, MA: Jones and Bartlett Publishers.

Biscontini, L. (2008). *Running the Show: Excellence in Service*. United States: FG2000 and Lulu.com.

Biscontini, L. (2009). *Cream Rises: Excellence in Private and Group Fitness Education*. United States: FG2000 and Lulu.com.

Carnegie, Dale (1981). *How to Win Friends and Influence People*. New York: Simon & Schuster Adult Publishing Group.

Churchill, G, & Peter, J. (1998). *Marketing: Creating Value for Customers*. Boston, MA: McGraw-Hill.

Pride, W., & Ferrell, O. (2008). *Marketing*. New York: Houghton Mifflin.

Pride, W., & Ferrell, O. (2006). *Marketing*. New York: Houghton Mifflin.

Periodicals

BusinessWeek magazine
Success magazine
The Wall Street Journal

About the Authors

Jeremy Koerber, MA, personifies the essence of marketing and customer service in the health and fitness industry. His philosophy is to find opportunities to serve in every capacity, making a trip to his fitness center or a session with Jeremy more than just an exercise session; it is an experience. His belief is to listen and understand the needs of his customers so he can provide products and services that satisfy those needs. Koerber understands the customer is the lifeblood to any organization, so to own a profitable personal-training business, you must meet and exceed customer expectations.

Koerber is the fitness-center manager for the BJC WellAware Center, a medically-based fitness facility associated with BJC HealthCare, one of the largest nonprofit health-care organizations in the United States. He is the owner of Integrated Wellness Concepts, LLC, a personal-training company serving West St. Louis County. Koerber is also an adjunct instructor at the Goldfarb School of Nursing at Barnes-Jewish College, where he teaches marketing and customer service skills to health-care professionals.

Koerber holds an undergraduate degree in health promotion from Southeast Missouri State University and a masters degree in marketing from Webster University. He is certified by the American College of Sports Medicine as a health fitness specialist and has over 12 years in the fitness industry. Koerber resides in St. Louis, Missouri, with his wife and two sons.

Kathy Bretsch, MBA, is the owner of Bretsch Communications Consulting, a firm providing communications solutions for organizations that want to be proactive about ensuring strategic, strong internal communications. Bretsch's professional career in corporate communications, marketing, and writing spans nearly 20 years, with 12 years in the health-care industry. She currently consults for several large health-care organizations.

Bretsch has an unbridled passion for fitness and a first-hand understanding of what the customer wants in a personal trainer: a trainer who is tuned into her needs and builds the training session into a relationship, a partnership. She believes that knowledge is power, and that as educated fitness professionals, you consciously make the choice at each and every session either to exceed customer expectations or to just show up. Those who exceed expectations will succeed.

Bretsch earned a bachelor's degree in journalism/mass communications and a masters degree in business administration, both from Southern Illinois University at Edwardsville. She's a lifelong fitness enthusiast who enjoys running, competing in sprint triathlons and practicing yoga, encouraging everyone she meets to join her. Bretsch resides in St. Louis, Missouri, with her husband and two children.